Name Reactions in
Organic Chemistry

Name Reactions in
Organic Chemistry

Alexander R. Surrey

Sterling-Winthrop Research Institute
Rensselaer, New York

2nd Edition
revised and enlarged

1961

ACADEMIC PRESS

New York and London

ACADEMIC PRESS INC.
111 FIFTH AVENUE
NEW YORK 3, N. Y.

United Kingdom Edition
Published by
ACADEMIC PRESS INC. (LONDON) LTD.
17 OLD QUEEN STREET, LONDON S.W. 1

Library of Congress Catalog Card Number 54-7611

PRINTED IN THE UNITED STATES OF AMERICA

Preface to Second Edition

In the relatively short time since the publication of the first edition of this book in 1954, numerous reviews and papers have been published dealing with various aspects of many "Name Reactions." It appeared therefore, that, rather than accept the simple expediency of a second printing, it would be advantageous and worthwhile to undertake an extensive revision of the first edition.

The author has attempted to incorporate new, pertinent material and to bring up to date the reactions described in the first edition. Along with this revision, several additional name reactions have been included. The same criteria as mentioned in the Preface to the first edition served as a guide in the choice of these reactions.

A.R.S.

Preface to First Edition

In the literature of organic chemistry there is a time-honored custom of designating many reactions by the names of the chemists who discovered or developed them. These "name reactions" constitute a considerable portion of the tools available to the organic chemist. Since their discovery these reactions have been applied in organic syntheses in varying degrees, and many have been modified. New procedures, reaction conditions, solvents, and condensing agents all have contributed to their development and improvement. In addition, investigations of mechanisms have led to a better understanding of many of them. As a result, the organic chemist today has at his disposal tools that have been sharpened and polished. It seemed worthwhile, therefore, to assemble these reactions and make them available to the chemist in their present state. The general plan was to present a description of each reaction, its scope, applicability, and limitations, and to bring it up to date in regard to any new developments.

The choice of the name reactions covered in this book may perhaps be questioned. No two chemists will agree completely as to which should be included. The writer's selections were made on the basis of general interest, recurrence in the literature, and the contributions of the "name chemist" to the historical development of organic chemistry.

With the rapid growth of organic chemistry, we tend to lose sight of the men who were the pioneers in the field. In this connection, Dr. R. E. Oesper, noted historian of chemistry, stated,* "Most chemists use names merely as convenient appellations for texts, laws, reactions, types of equipment. Usually no thought is given to the man whose name is so glibly employed. One of the duties of the historian of chemistry is to convert a name into a person."

Although the writer does not pretend to be an historian of chemistry, it seemed desirable to include, along with the reactions, pertinent information regarding the chemist's background, his training, his contemporaries, and his contributions. It is hoped that these sketches,

* *Journal of Chemical Education,* **19,** 444 (1942).

which are part of the history of chemistry, may be of interest to the reader.

An extensive or complete coverage of the literature for each reaction is beyond the scope of this book. No attempt has been made to compete with "Organic Reactions," nor has any effort been made to cite references solely on the basis of priority. Rather, the selection has been made from the viewpoint of general interest, illustrative examples, and leading references. Citations up to January 1, 1953, are included; in a few instances later references were added. From these, the reader can obtain recent experimental procedures and, in many instances, general reviews. A general index is included, which, it is hoped, will be of value to the research chemist in searching for types of reactions pertinent to his immediate problems.

The principal sources of the biographical data included in this book were Poggendorff's "Biographisch-Literarisches Handwörterbuch, *Chemische Berichte, Bulletin de la Société Chimique de France, Journal of Chemical Education, Journal of the Chemical Society of London,* personal columns of foreign journals, and personal correspondence.

The author is indebted to Dr. W. S. Johnson of the University of Wisconsin, and Dr. C. F. Koelsch of the University of Minnesota, for reading most of the manuscript and for giving valuable suggestions and encouragement during the preparation of this book. He wishes to express his appreciation to Dr. E. J. Lawson, Dr. C. M. Suter, and Dr. M. L. Tainter for their interest in this work and for placing the facilities of the Sterling-Winthrop Research Institute at his disposal. Thanks are also due to Dr. F. C. Nachod for his generous assistance, especially in the translation of some of the biographical material, and to several other colleagues in this Institute for their cooperation throughout.

ALEXANDER R. SURREY

Table of Contents

CONTENTS

Arndt-Eistert Synthesis

Fritz Arndt (1885–   ) was born in Hamburg, Germany. He studied at Geneva, Berlin, and Freiburg, where he received his doctor's degree in 1908 as a student of J. Howitz. After serving as an assistant at Greifswald, Freiburg, and Kiel, Arndt served as professor at the University of Istanbul during the first World War. In 1920, he was appointed professor at Breslau. He left Germany in 1933, and for a year was guest professor at Oxford before returning to the University of Istanbul.

Arndt's important contributions to resonance theory have been reported.[1] He worked on a variety of problems, and has been particularly interested in the synthesis of diazomethane, and its reactions with aldehydes, ketones, and acid chlorides.

*   *   *

Bernd Eistert (1902–   ) was born in Ohlau, Silesia. At the University of Breslau he studied under F. Arndt and H. Biltz and received the Ph.D. degree in 1927. After serving as an assistant to Arndt, and then to P. Pfeiffer at Bonn, Eistert became associated with the Badische Anilin und Soda-Fabrik at Ludwigshafen, where he is still employed. In 1942 he joined the faculty at Heidelberg and then at the Technische Hochschule in Darmstadt, where eight years later he was appointed adjunct professor.

In addition to his work on the diazo compounds, Eistert has been interested in the relationship of structure and color. Among his publications are the books "Tautomerie und Mesomerie" and "Chemismus und Konstitution." In 1951, Eistert was awarded the Scheele Medal by the Stockholm Chemical Society.

When an acid is converted to its acid chloride and the chloride is allowed to react with diazomethane, a diazomethyl ketone is formed. Decomposition of the diazo ketone with silver oxide in the presence of water gives the next higher homologous acid. This sequence of reactions is known as the Arndt-Eistert synthesis.[2,3]

$$RCOOH \xrightarrow{SOCl_2} RCOCl \xrightarrow{CH_2N_2} RCOCHN_2$$

$$RCOCHN_2 \xrightarrow[H_2O]{Ag_2O} RCH_2COOH$$

Part of the synthesis, involving the rearrangement of a diazo ketone into an acid derivative, is known as the *Wolff rearrangement*.[4] The procedure for this rearrangement has been improved by Newman and Beal,[5] who showed that with a solution of silver benzoate in triethylamine the reaction medium is homogeneous. The diazo ketone is most probably converted to a ketene which reacts with water or other material in the reaction mixture in the following manner:

$$RCOCHN_2 \longrightarrow RCH{=}C{=}O$$

$$RCH{=}C{=}O \xrightarrow{H_2O} RCH_2COOH$$

$$RCH{=}C{=}O \xrightarrow{NH_3} RCH_2CONH_2$$

$$RCH{=}C{=}O \xrightarrow{R'OH} RCH_2COOR'$$

The Arndt-Eistert synthesis is applicable to aliphatic, aromatic, acyclic, and heterocyclic carboxylic acids. The diazo ketone is prepared by adding the acid chloride to an excess of diazomethane in ether or benzene solution (a). Hydrogen chloride formed in the reaction is removed by diazomethane (b). In the absence of an excess of diazomethane a chloro ketone is formed (c).

$$\text{(a)}\ RCOCl + CH_2N_2 \longrightarrow RCOCHN_2 + HCl$$

$$\text{(b)}\ HCl + CH_2N_2 \longrightarrow CH_3Cl + N_2$$

$$\text{(c)}\ RCOCHN_2 + HCl \longrightarrow RCOCH_2Cl + N_2$$

Newman and Beal[6] have shown that with aromatic acid chlorides the use of one equivalent each of diazomethane and triethylamine gives excellent yields of diazo ketones. The formation of aryl chloromethyl ketones by the reaction of an aroyl chloride and diazomethane is often referred to as the *Nierenstein reaction*.[7]

In the presence of silver benzoate-triethylamine catalyst, a variety of unsaturated acids have been converted into their next higher homologs by the Arndt-Eistert sequence.[8] The yields were very satisfactory for the acids in which the unsaturation was in a position other than α,β.

The stereochemistry of the *Wolff rearrangement* has recently been investigated by Wiberg and Hutton.[9] With *sec*-alkyl diazomethyl ketones the rearrangement proceeds largely with retention of configuration.

The use of higher diazo hydrocarbons in the Arndt-Eistert synthesis has been reported by Wilds and Meader.[10] For example, the reaction of diazoethane with *p*-chlorobenzoyl chloride gave a diazo ketone which was rearranged by heating in aniline.

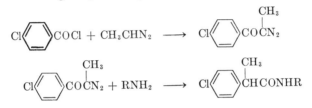

Rearrangement was also effected by heating in dimethylaniline in the presence of benzyl alcohol to give the benzyl ester. The usual reaction, using silver oxide, failed in these instances.

References

1. E. Campaigne, *J. Chem. Educ.* **36**, 336 (1959).
2. F. Arndt and B. Eistert, *Ber. deut. Chem. Ges.* **68**, 200 (1935).
3. A review of the Arndt-Eistert synthesis is given by W. E. Bachmann and W. S. Struve, *in* "Organic Reactions" (R. Adams, ed.), Vol. I, p. 38. Wiley, New York, 1942.
4. L. Wolff, *Ann. Chem. Liebigs* **394**, 25 (1912).
5. M. S. Newman and P. F. Beal, *J. Am. Chem. Soc.* **72**, 5163 (1950).
6. M. S. Newman and P. F. Beal, *J. Am. Chem. Soc.* **71**, 1506 (1949).
7. D. A. Clibbens and M. Nierenstein, *J. Chem. Soc.* **107**, 1491 (1915); M. Nierenstein, D. G. Wang, and J. C. Warr, *J. Am. Chem. Soc.* **46**, 2551 (1924).
8. J. H. Wotiz and S. N. Buco, *J. Org. Chem.* **20**, 210 (1955).
9. K. B. Wiberg and T. W. Hutton, *J. Am. Chem. Soc.* **78**, 1640 (1956).
10. A. L. Wilds and A. L. Meader, *J. Org. Chem.* **13**, 763 (1948).

Baeyer-Villiger Oxidation

Adolf von Baeyer (1835–1917) was born in Berlin, Germany. He studied at Berlin, at Heidelberg with Bunsen, and then with Kekulé. In 1858 he received his doctor's degree at Berlin, and joined the faculty there under Hofmann. In 1872 Baeyer was called to Strassburg as professor of chemistry and director of the new chemical laboratories, and three years later he succeeded von Liebig at Munich. Baeyer attracted organic chemists from all over the world. His teaching continued right up to his eightieth birthday. He was succeeded to the chair of chemistry by Willstätter, one of his distinguished students, who received the Nobel Prize in 1915 for his work on chlorophyll.

Baeyer is certainly known as one of the great men of modern organic chemistry. His interests and researches were widespread. Every organic chemist is familiar with his outstanding work on the elucidation of the structure and synthesis of indigo. Some of his other investigations were with the phthaleins, uric acid, terpenes, purines, and the structure of benzene. In 1905, he received the Nobel Prize for his work on organic dyes, and hydroaromatic compounds.

The oxidation of aldehydes and ketones with hydrogen peroxide or peracids to yield esters or derivatives therefrom is known as the Baeyer-Villiger[1,2] oxidation. The reaction is represented by the following equation:

$$R-\overset{\overset{\text{O}}{\|}}{C}-R' \quad \xrightarrow[\text{Peracids}]{\text{H}_2\text{O}_2 \text{ or}} \quad R-\overset{\overset{\text{O}}{\|}}{C}-OR'$$

The original work by Baeyer and Villiger in 1899 dealt with the oxidation of alicyclic ketones with peroxymonosulfuric acid to form lactones. One of the cyclic ketones used was menthone.

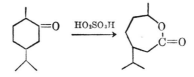

An ionic mechanism for the reaction was proposed by Criegee in 1948.[3] The first step probably involves the addition of the peroxide to the carbonyl group. The R group with its pair of electrons migrates to oxygen wtih cleavage of R″O⁻ from the peroxide linkage, and loss of a proton results in the formation of the ester. Rearrangement occurs with retention of configuration.

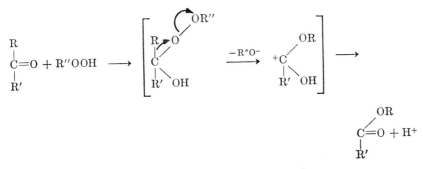

It has been shown that with diaryl ketones the migratory group will be the one with the greatest electron donating capacity.[4] For example, with p-methoxybenzophenone the reaction with peroxybenzoic acid yields hydroquinone monomethyl ether and benzoic acid. The p-methoxyphenyl group is the migratory group.

A variety of solvents have been used in the Baeyer-Villiger reaction depending upon the solubilities of the reactants. With peroxybenzoic acid the preferred solvent appears to be chloroform. The peracids used include peroxybenzoic, peroxymonophthalic, peroxymonosulfuric, and peroxyacetic. For the most part, the reaction conditions are mild and the yields are satisfactory.

Trifluoroperoxyacetic acid, in the presence of dibasic sodium phosphate, has been found to be an excellent reagent for the oxidation of ketones to esters.[5] Methyl cyclopropyl ketone has been oxidized in this manner to cyclopropyl acetate in 53% yield.

In the oxidation of methyl alkyl ketones it has been shown that the alkyl group is the only one which migrates.

Alicyclic ketones from $n = 1$ to $n = 14$ have been oxidized with peracids to give lactones. In the presence of ethyl alcohol the products are ethyl esters of ω-hydroxy acids.

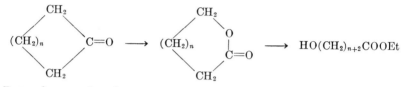

Butyrolactone has been prepared by this method in 70% yield from cyclobutanone.[6]

Aliphatic and aromatic aldehydes are usually converted to carboxylic acids upon treatment with peracids. The oxidation of aromatic aldehydes having a methoxy or hydroxy group in the *ortho* or *para* position with hydrogen peroxide in alkaline solution leads to a replacement of the aldehyde group by a hydroxyl group. This is a modification of the Baeyer-Villiger oxidation known as the Dakin reaction (see page 64).

References

1. A. Baeyer and Villiger, *Ber. deut. Chem. Ges.* **32**, 3625 (1899).
2. A review of the Baeyer-Villiger oxidation is given by C. H. Hassall, *in* "Organic Reactions" (R. Adams, ed.), Vol. IX, p. 73. Wiley, New York, 1957.
3. R. Criegee, *Ann. Chem. Liebigs* **560**, 127 (1948).
4. W. E. Doering and E. Dorfman, *J. Am. Chem. Soc.* **75**, 5595 (1953).
5. W. D. Emmons and G. B. Lucas, *J. Am. Chem. Soc.* **77**, 2287 (1955).
6. S. L. Friess and P. E. Frankenburg, *J. Am. Chem. Soc.* **74**, 2679 (1952).

Barbier-Wieland Degradation

Phillippe Antoine Barbier (1848–1922) was born in Luzy, Nièvre, France. He received the Doctor of Science degree in 1876 at the Collège de France, where Berthelot was professor of chemistry. In 1880, he was appointed professor of general chemistry at Besançon, and from 1884 to 1919 he held a similar position at Lyons.

Barbier worked on a large number of problems. It was in connection with his investigations in the terpene field that he attempted the reaction of methylheptenone with methyl iodide in the presence of zinc. The reaction was unsuccessful. When magnesium was used, however, a vigorous reaction resulted and dimethylheptenol was obtained. Barbier suggested the use of magnesium to Grignard, his student, in connection with some of the latter's work. The results are history.

* * *

Heinrich Wieland (1877–1957) was born at Pforzheim, Baden. He studied at Berlin, at Stuttgart, and under J. Thiele at Munich. There, in 1901, Wieland received his doctorate degree, and in 1909 was appointed professor of chemistry. Later he held similar positions at the Technische Hochschule in Munich, and at Freiburg. In 1925, Wieland returned to Munich to succeed R. Willstätter.

Wieland was one of the pioneers in the field of organic nitrogen chemistry. He did considerable work on the structures of nitrogenous products. In 1927, he was awarded the Nobel Prize for chemistry for his outstanding work on bile acids, organic radicals, and nitrogen compounds. Wieland's contributions to biochemistry include his research on the mechanisms of biological oxidation.

His brother, the late Hermann Wieland, was professor of pharmacology at the University of Heidelberg.

A method of converting an acid to the next lower homolog by the following sequence of reactions is called the Barbier-Wieland degradation.[1]

$$\underset{\text{I}}{RCH_2COOH} \longrightarrow \underset{\text{II}}{RCH_2COOCH_3} \xrightarrow{C_6H_5MgBr} \underset{\text{III}}{RCH_2\overset{\overset{\displaystyle OH}{|}}{C}(C_6H_5)_2} \xrightarrow{-H_2O}$$

$$\underset{\text{IV}}{RCH=C(C_6H_5)_2} \xrightarrow{CrO_3} \underset{\text{V}}{RCOOH} + (C_6H_5)_2CO$$

Reaction of the ester with phenylmagnesium bromide yields the tertiary alcohol (III), which loses water on heating with acetic anhydride to give the unsaturated compound (IV). Oxidation with chromic anhydride in acetic acid gives the acid (V). An example of the Barbier-Wieland degradation is the conversion of *cis*-2-phenyl-cyclohexaneacetic acid to *cis*-2-phenylcyclohexanecarboxylic acid.[2]

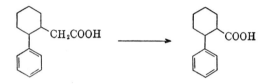

The Barbier-Wieland degradation has been especially useful in the stepwise degradation of sterol side chains. Many variations of this method have been employed.[3] The Miescher modification,[4] in which three carbon atoms are eliminated at one time, is particularly useful.

$$\underset{\text{}}{R-\overset{\overset{\displaystyle CH_3}{|}}{C}H-CH_2-CH=C(C_6H_5)_2} \xrightarrow[\text{succinimide}]{\text{N-bromo-}} R-\overset{\overset{\displaystyle CH_3}{|}}{C}H-\overset{\overset{\displaystyle Br}{|}}{C}H-CH=C(C_6H_5)_2$$

$$\xrightarrow{-HBr} R-\overset{\overset{\displaystyle CH_3}{|}}{C}=CH-CH=C(C_6H_5)_2 \xrightarrow{CrO_3} R-COCH_3$$

It has recently been reported[5] that chromic acid oxidation of the tertiary alcohol (VI) in acetic acid-water gives only a small yield of the expected acid (VII). The major product is the ketone, 4-methyl-4-phenyl-2-pentanone (VIII).

$$\underset{\text{VI}}{C_6H_5C(CH_3)_2CH_2C(CH_3)_2OH} \xrightarrow{CrO_3}$$

$$\underset{\text{VIII}}{C_6H_5C(CH_3)_2CH_2COCH_3} + \underset{\text{VII}}{C_6H_5C(CH_3)_2COOH}$$

8

References

1. P. Barbier and R. Locquin, *Compt. rend. Acad. Sci.* **156,** 1443 (1913); H. Wieland, O. Schlichting, and R. Jacobi, Z. *physiol. Chem.* **161,** 80 (1926).
2. C. D. Gutsche, *J. Am. Chem. Soc.* **70,** 4150 (1948).
3. C. W. Shoppee, *Ann. Repts. on Progr. Chem.* (*Chem. Soc. London*) **44,** 184 (1947).
4. C. Meystre, H. Frey, A. Wettstein, and K. Miescher, *Helv. Chim. Acta* **27,** 1815 (1944).
5. W. Baker, R. F. Curtis, J. F. W. McOmie, L. W. Olive, and V. Rogers, *J. Chem. Soc.* p. 1007 (1958).

Bart Reaction

Heinrich Bart was interested in the preparation of arsenical compounds for the treatment of protozoan infections. He began his investigation on methods of synthesizing aromatic arsenic acids in 1909. In 1922, Bart published a great deal of his results from the Biochemical Institute of the University of Heidelberg.

The conversion of an aromatic diazonium salt to the corresponding arsonic acid by treatment with sodium arsenite in the presence of a catalyst such as copper or a copper salt is called the Bart reaction.[1] An illustration is the preparation of benzenearsonic acid from benzenediazonium chloride.

$$C_6H_5N_2Cl + Na_3AsO_3 \xrightarrow{Cu} C_6H_5AsO_3Na_2 + NaCl + N_2$$

The reaction is performed by adding the solution of the diazonium salt to an alkaline solution of sodium arsenite containing the catalyst. The mixture is allowed to stand or is warmed until no further evolution of nitrogen occurs, and is then acidified to precipitate the product.

There have been many modifications of the Bart reaction.[2] The reaction has been carried out in neutral solution without a catalyst or in a buffered solution in the presence of a catalyst. The optimum conditions vary with the position and nature of substituents on the aromatic nucleus.

The decomposition of diazonium fluoborates with sodium arsenite has proved to be a useful modification of the Bart reaction.[3] The fluoborate salt prepared by diazotization of the aromatic amine in the presence of fluoroboric acid[4] is added to an aqueous solution of sodium arsenite containing cuprous chloride. With p-nitrobenzenediazonium fluoborate, the yield of *p*-nitrobenzenearsonic acid is 79%.[5]

$$p\text{-}NO_2C_6H_4N_2BF_4 \longrightarrow p\text{-}NO_2C_6H_4AsO_3Na_2$$

References

1. H. Bart, German Patents 250,264, 254,092, 264,924 (1910); 268,172 (1912).
2. For a review of the Bart reaction, see C. S. Hamilton and J. F. Morgan, *in* "Organic Reactions" (R. Adams, ed.), Vol. II, p. 415. Wiley, New York, 1944.
3. A. W. Ruddy, E. B. Starkey, and W. H. Hartung, *J. Am. Chem. Soc.* **64**, 828 (1942).
4. See Schiemann reaction p. 213.
5. A. W. Ruddy and E. B. Starkey, *in* "Organic Syntheses" (H. Adkins, ed.), Vol. 26, p. 60. Wiley, New York, 1946.

Béchamp Reduction

Antoine J. Béchamp (1816–1908) was born in Bassing, France. He received the Doctor of Science degree in 1853 and the Doctor of Medicine degree in 1856. The following year he became professor of chemistry and pharmacy at Montpellier and later served on the faculties at Nancy and Lille.

Béchamp was a prolific worker. He investigated the action of enzymes, wine fermentation, and many other problems in biochemistry. His discovery of the reduction of nitrobenzene with iron and dilute acid was an important one in the development of the dye industry. Perkin used this process in his manufacture of the dye, mauve.

Béchamp prepared arsanilic acid (1863) by heating aniline and aniline arsenite. The structure of the compound and the nature of the reaction was demonstrated by Ehrlich and Bertheim. The formation of arylarsonic acids by heating an arylamine or phenol with arsenic acid is now known as the Béchamp reaction.[1]

The chemical reduction of nitro compounds to the corresponding amines by means of iron or ferrous salts and dilute acid is referred to as the Béchamp reduction.[2] Because the method is economical and simple, it has had wide application in industrial processes.[3] A large variety of aromatic nitro compounds have been reduced by the Béchamp method.

A useful procedure in the laboratory involves the addition of the nitro compound to a well-stirred, refluxing mixture of iron filings in alcohol-water containing a small amount of acetic acid. The rate of addition of the nitro compound depends upon the exothermal nature of the reaction. The alcohol-water ratio can be varied according to the solubility of the nitro compound. Refluxing is continued until an iron mirror is formed on the inside of the flask. When the reaction is completed, the mixture is treated with solid sodium carbonate and filtered. The product is usually obtained by distilling off the alcohol. An example of this method is the reduction of 4-amino-7-chloro-3-nitroquinoline to 7-chloro-3,4-diaminoquinoline in 75% yield.[4]

The use of ferrous sulfate is illustrated in the conversion of p-nitrosalicylic acid to p-aminosalicylic acid.[5]

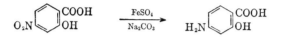

References

1. See C. F. Hamilton and J. F. Morgan, in "Organic Reactions" (R. Adams, ed.), Vol. II, p. 415. Wiley, New York, 1944.
2. A. J. Béchamp, Ann. chim. et phys. [3] 42, 186 (1854).
3. J. Werner, Ind. Eng. Chem. 43, 1917 (1951).
4. A. R. Surrey and R. A. Cutler, J. Am. Chem. Soc. 73, 2413 (1951).
5. J. F. McGhie, C. Morton, B. L. Reynolds, and J. W. Spense, J. Soc. Chem. Ind. (London) 68, 328 (1949).

Beckmann Rearrangement

Ernst Otto Beckmann (1853–1923) was born in Solingen, Germany. He was a student of Kolbe at Leipzig, where he received the doctor's degree in 1878. When Kolbe died he was succeeded by Wislicenus, who appointed Beckmann his assistant. Under Wislicenus, Beckmann studied the spatial arrangements of the oximes of menthone which led to the discovery of the reaction which was named by Victor Meyer the "Beckmann rearrangement."

Beckmann was an outstanding teacher. He served as professor of chemistry at Erlangen and Leipzig and became director of the Kaiser Wilhelm-Institut für Chemie in 1912.

Beckmann's freezing and boiling point methods for the determination of molecular weights of organic compounds and the thermometer he devised which bears his name are well known to organic chemists.

The Beckmann rearrangement consists in the treatment of a ketoxime with a suitable reagent such as phosphorus pentachloride, benzenesulfonyl chloride, or sulfuric acid, to give a substituted amide.[1] The reaction was discovered in 1886 by Beckmann,[2] who found that benzophenone oxime reacts vigorously with phosphorus pentachloride to form benzanilide.

$$(C_6H_5)_2C{=}NOH \xrightarrow{\text{PCl}_5} C_6H_5CONHC_6H_5$$

A wide variety of reagents in addition to those mentioned above have been found capable of effecting the rearrangement. Among them are acetyl chloride, phosphorus oxychloride, chloral, and hydrogen chloride. Oxime ethers and esters are susceptible to this type of rearrangement.

The Beckmann rearrangement involves an interchange of the hydroxyl group of the oxime with the radical situated *anti* to it. For example, with an unsymmetrical ketoxime the rearrangement may be represented as follows:

$$R-\underset{\underset{NOH}{\|}}{C}-R' \longrightarrow HO-\underset{\underset{NR}{\|}}{C}-R' \longrightarrow R'CONHR$$

With a cyclic ketone, rearrangement of the oxime gives rise to a cyclic amide.

The Beckmann rearrangement has been represented as involving a *trans* shift with ionization of the acyl derivative of the oxime.[3]

The mechanism of the Beckmann rearrangement has been the subject of many investigations.[4] New evidence for an imidoyl ester type (I) as an intermediate has been obtained in the rearrangement of a 17-keto-16-oxime steroid.[5]

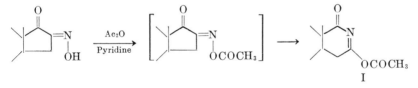

A mechanism involving the formation of a ketoxime anhydride, and rearrangement to an imidoyl anhydride has been proposed by Stephen and Staskun.[6]

$$2\ R_2C{=}NOH \longrightarrow (R_2C{=}N)_2O \longrightarrow (R-\underset{\underset{}{\overset{R}{|}}}{N}{=}C)_2O$$

The migration of a radical from carbon to nitrogen is similar to that encountered in the Hofmann and Curtius reactions. When an asymmetric carbon atom is involved, the Beckmann rearrangement occurs without change of configuration. This was demonstrated by Campbell and Kenyon[7] with (—)-α-phenylethyl methyl ketoxime.

15

$$\underset{\underset{NOH}{\overset{*}{\underset{\|}{C_6H_5-CH-C-CH_3}}}}{\overset{CH_3}{|}} \xrightarrow[\text{ether}]{H_2SO_4} \underset{\overset{*}{CH_3CONH-CH-C_6H_5}}{\overset{CH_3}{|}}$$

Horning[8,9] has recently shown that polyphosphoric acid is an excellent reagent for the Beckmann rearrangement with both ketoximes[8] and aldoximes.[9] With benzophenone oxime the yield of benzanilide was quantitative; with heptanal oxime a 92% yield of heptanamide was obtained.

References

1. For a review of the Beckmann rearrangement, see A. H. Blatt, *Chem. Revs.* **12**, 215 (1933).
2. E. Beckmann, *Ber. deut. Chem. Ges.* **19**, 988 (1886).
3. The rates of migration of different groups in the Beckmann rearrangement are given by A. W. Chapman and F. A. Fidler, *J. Chem. Soc.* p. 448 (1936).
4. For a review of the mechanism of the Beckmann rearrangement, see B. Jones, *Chem. Revs.* **35**, 335 (1944); see, also, E. R. Alexander, "Principles of Ionic Organic Reactions," p. 72, Wiley, New York, 1950.
5. R. D. H. Heard, M. T. Ryan, and H. I. Bolker, *J. Org. Chem.* **24**, 172 (1959).
6. H. Stephen and B. Staskun, *J. Chem. Soc.* p. 980 (1956).
7. A. Campbell and J. Kenyon, *J. Chem. Soc.* p. 25 (1946).
8. F. C. Horning and V. L. Stromberg, *J. Am. Chem. Soc.* **74**, 2680 (1952).
9. F. C. Horning and V. L. Stromberg, *J. Am. Chem. Soc.* **74**, 5151 (1952).

Birch Reduction

A. J. Birch (1915–   ) was born in Sydney, Australia. He studied at the University of Sydney, and then at Oxford University where he received his doctor's degree (1938) under Sir Robert Robinson. In 1949, Birch went to Cambridge as a Smithson Fellow of the Royal Society where he worked under Sir Alexander Todd. Three years later he returned to Sydney as professor of organic chemistry. Since 1958, he has been professor of organic chemistry at Manchester University.

Birch's main interest include reduction by metal-ammonia solutions, synthesis of steroid analogues, biosynthesis, and structures of natural products. He was elected fellow of the Australian Academy of Science in 1954, and fellow of the Royal Society in 1958.

The reduction of an aromatic compound in liquid ammonia with an alkali metal and an alcohol to give initially a 1,4-cyclohexadiene is commonly referred to as the Birch reduction.[1-3] Originally discovered by Wooster,[4] and further studied and developed by Birch, its usefulness lies in its wide scope, simplicity of procedure, and uniqueness of products. The reaction has been applied to many classes of compounds[5] including methoxybenzenes, benzoic acids, naphthoic acids, naphthols, heterocyclic compounds, amidines, imidazoles, and steroids.

The general procedure involves the addition of sodium to a mixture containing the compound to be reduced, liquid ammonia, and absolute alcohol. Frequently a co-solvent such as ether, tetrahydrofuran, or 1,2-dimethoxyethane is used to increase solubility, and occasionally the alcohol is added last. For example, 2-methoxy-5,6,7,8-tetrahydronaphthalene (I) may be reduced to the enol ether (II). Mild hydrolysis of II gives the unconjugated ketone (III), and further treatment with acid or base gives the conjugated ketone

4,4a,5,6,7,8-hexahydro-2 (3H)-naphthalenone (IV) in 82% yield based on I.[1]

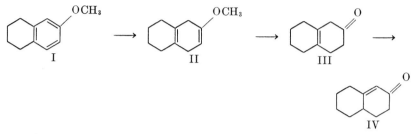

The important modification of the Birch reduction involves the substitution of lithium for sodium.[6] The ease with which this procedure effects otherwise difficult reductions renders it superior. In the original example studied by Wilds and Nelson,[6] ordinary Birch conditions failed to reduce 4-cyclohexylanisole (V). By using lithium, and adding the alcohol last, a yield of 88% of the crystalline dihydro compound (VI) was obtained.

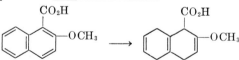

The Birch reduction of 2-naphthoic acid, and its 1- and 3-methoxy derivatives gives mainly 1,2,3,4-tetrahydro-2-naphthoic acid, and 1,2,3,4,5,8-hexahydronaphthoic acid depending upon the conditions and proportions of the reactants.[7] 2-Methoxy-1-naphthoic acid gives 2-methoxy-1,4,5,8-tetrahydro-1-naphthoic acid without loss of the methoxy group.[7]

An application of the Birch reduction under forcing conditions is described by Johnson et al.[8] in the reduction of the aromatic nucleus of a dodecahydrochrysene derivative. The procedure involves the use of a relatively high proportion of alcohol, and the controlled addition of lithium to the reaction mixture so as to effect and maintain the separation of a bronze-colored phase which forms at higher concentrations of metal in ammonia.

18

The theoretical background for the Birch reduction has been presented,[2] and recently several investigations dealing with the mechanism of the reduction have been published.[5,9,10] The mechanism favored by Krapcho and Bothner-By[5] is as follows, where M is an alkali metal, S is the solvent (liquid ammonia), (s) indicates solvation and ROH is an alcohol:

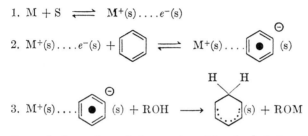

The reaction of the solvated ion pair with alcohol to give metal alkoxide and a radical intermediate is the rate-determining step. This intermediate reacts further in a similar manner to give the dihydro derivative.

Kuehne and Lambert[10] have investigated the effect of substituents which have a stabilizing or destabilizing effect on negative charges and radicals in the Birch reduction of aromatic acids and amides. These authors have shown that the position of the double bonds in the reduced products depends on the protonization of the carbanions at the site of maximum charge density and the stability of the products.

References

1. A. J. Birch, *J. Chem. Soc.* p. 430 (1944); *J. Chem. Soc.* p. 593 (1946).
2. A. J. Birch, *Quart. Revs. (London)* 4, 69 (1950).
3. A. J. Birch and H. Smith, *Quart. Revs. (London)* 12, 17 (1958).
4. C. B. Wooster, U. S. Patent 2,182,242 (1939); C. B. Wooster and K. L. Godfrey, *J. Am. Chem. Soc.* 59, 596 (1937).
5. A. P. Krapcho and A. A. Bothner-By, *J. Am. Chem. Soc.* 81, 3658 (1959).
6. A. L. Wilds and N. A. Nelson, *J. Am. Chem. Soc.* 75, 5360 (1953).
7. E. L. Eliel and T. E. Hoover, *J. Org. Chem.* 24, 938 (1959).
8. W. S. Johnson, B. Bannister, and R. Pappo, *J. Am. Chem. Soc.* 78, 6331 (1956).
9. A. J. Birch and D. Nasipuri, *Tetrahedron* 6, 148 (1959).
10. M. E. Kuehne and B. F. Lambert, *J. Am. Chem. Soc.* 81, 4278 (1959).

Bischler-Napieralski Reaction

Augustus Bischler (1865–1957) was born in South Russia of Alsace-Lorraine origin. He studied chemistry at the Polytechnikum at Zurich under Victor Meyer and A. Hantzsch. After receiving his Ph.D. degree under V. Merz, he became an assistant professor. His interest in alkaloids led to the discovery of the isoquinoline synthesis. B. Napieralski was one of the candidates for the doctorate who worked under Bischler.

After several years, Bischler left the University to become chemical director of Ciba Ltd. in Basel (1897–1910) and then director of a factory in Monthey. He continued his activities in different laboratories until 1955.

When an acyl derivative of a phenethylamine is treated with a dehydrating agent such as phosphorus oxychloride, phosphorus pentoxide, or polyphosphoric acid, cyclodehydration occurs, with the formation of a 3,4-dihydroisoquinoline.

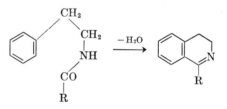

This reaction, which was discovered by Bischler and Napieralski[1] in 1893, is a valuable method for the preparation of a large number of isoquinoline compounds, especially those in the alkaloid field.[2,3]

Aryl, aralkyl, and alkyl amides have been successfully employed in the Bischler-Napieralski reaction. The usual procedure is to heat the amide with a dehydrating agent[4] in an inert solvent such as chloroform, benzene, toluene, or nitrobenzene. The selection of the solvent is dependent upon the desired reflux temperature. Isolation of the 3,4-dihydroisoquinoline is usually effected by steam distillation or extraction.

The mechanism of the Bischler-Napieralski reaction probably involves an electrophilic attack by the carbonyl carbon atom at an *ortho* position to the aminoethyl grouping. This is illustrated by an activated phenethylamine, one containing an alkoxy group in the *meta* position.

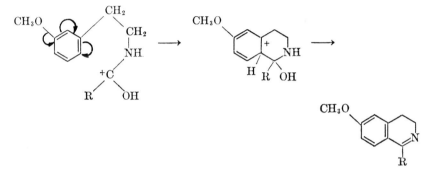

Dehydrogenation of the 3,4-dihydro compounds leads to isoquinolines. By employing a β-hydroxyphenethylamide, the isoquinoline may be obtained directly. This modification is known as the *Pictet-Gams synthesis*.[5] It involves the initial formation of a styrylamide which is further dehydrated to give the isoquinoline.

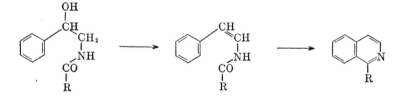

A recent application[6] of the Bischler-Napieralski reaction is the preparation of a substituted benzophenone, a possible intermediate in the synthesis of picropodophyllin. The dihydroisoquinoline (I) prepared by the usual procedure was treated with dimethyl sulfate and excess sodium hydroxide.

21

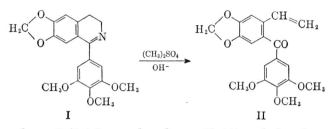

I   II

The product, 2-(3,4,5-trimethoxybenzoyl)-4,5-methylenedioxystyrene (II) was obtained in excellent yield.

The Bischler-Napieralski reaction has also been applied to some cyclohexenylethylamines for the preparation of octahydroisoquinolines.[7] Isoquinolines have also been prepared from cyclohexadiene

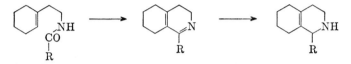

derivatives.[8] The dihydro compound III, prepared by a Birch reduction, was treated with 3,4-dimethoxyphenylacetyl chloride and the

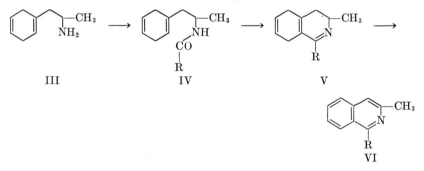

III   IV   V

VI

resulting amide (IV) was cyclized using phosphorus oxychloride in benzene. The product (V) was dehydrogenated in two steps; (a) with Pd-C in xylene, and (b) with Pd-C and ethyl cinnamate, to give the isoquinoline (VI).

Pyridine derivatives have now been synthesized by cyclization of acyl derivatives of 5-phenyl-4-pentenylamine.[9]

$$C_6H_5CH=CHCH_2CH_2CH_2NHCOR \longrightarrow$$

References

1. A. Bischler and B. Napieralski, *Ber. deut. Chem. Ges.* **26**, 1903 (1893).
2. For a review of the Bischler-Napieralski reaction, see W. M. Whaley and T. R. Govindachari, *in* "Organic Reactions" (R. Adams, ed.), Vol. VI, p. 74. Wiley, New York, 1951.
3. See also W. J. Gensler, *in* "Heterocyclic Compounds" (R. C. Elderfield, ed.), Vol. 4, pp. 347–353. Wiley, New York, 1952.
4. A new combination, phosphorus pentoxide-pyridine with sand, for the Bischler-Napieralski reaction is described by N. Itoh and S. Sugasawa, *Tetrahedron* **1**, 45 (1957).
5. A. Pictet and A. Gams, *Ber. deut. Chem. Ges.* **42**, 2943 (1909); see also W. M. Whaley and T. R. Govindachari, *in* "Organic Reactions" (R. Adams, ed.), Vol. VI, p. 361. Wiley, New York, 1951.
6. W. J. Gensler and C. M. Samour, *J. Am. Chem. Soc.* **73**, 5555 (1951).
7. O. Schnider and J. Hellerbach, *Helv. Chim. Acta* **34**, 2218 (1951).
8. R. Tachikawa, *Tetrahedron* **7**, 118 (1959).
9. T. Fuyisawa and S. Sugasawa, *Tetrahedron* **7**, 185 (1959).

Blanc Chloromethylation Reaction

Gustave Louis Blanc (1872–1927) was born in Paris, France, where he studied at the School of Physics and Industrial Chemistry. He became an assistant on the Faculté des Sciences at Paris, where in 1899 he obtained his doctorate in science. From 1906 he directed the technical laboratories of the Intendence militaire aux Invalides.

Blanc was interested in the chemistry of terpenes as well as in aliphatic and hydroaromatic chemistry. It was during his investigation of some camphor derivatives that Blanc obtained an alcohol from the reaction of an ester with sodium and alcohol. He found that fatty esters were reduced in a similar manner. In collaboration with Bouveault, the general method of sodium and alcohol reduction of esters was developed.

Blanc developed a general procedure for the chloromethylation of aromatic hydrocarbons which was employed in the preparation of benzyl alcohol, and toluene. He also prepared benzaldehyde from benzyl alcohol by oxidation with bichromate.

The process of chloromethylation of aromatic compounds by treatment with formaldehyde and hydrogen chloride in the presence of zinc chloride is frequently referred to as the Blanc reaction.[1,2] The method may be illustrated by the preparation of benzyl chloride from benzene.

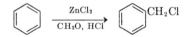

Dry hydrogen chloride gas is passed into a mixture of benzene, paraformaldehyde, and zinc chloride at 60° until no more gas is absorbed. Benzyl chloride is obtained in a 79% yield. Another example is the formation of 1-chloromethylnaphthalene from naphthalene.[3]

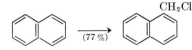

Other catalysts, such as sulfuric acid, phosphoric acid, and aluminum chloride, have also been used. The most important side reaction is the formation of diarylmethanes. Chloromethylation in the presence of arsenous chloride or arsenous oxide is claimed to inhibit the formation of diarylmethanes and other by-products.[4] By this procedure, naphthalene is converted to 1-chloromethylnaphthalene in about 90% yield based on recovered naphthalene.

Chloromethylation of methyl 2-furoate gives an 83% yield of methyl 5-chloromethyl-2-furoate.[5]

$$\text{COOCH}_3 \xrightarrow[\text{CH}_2\text{O, HCl}]{\text{ZnCl}_2} \text{ClCH}_2\text{—}\text{COOCH}_3$$

An illustration of the introduction of two chloromethyl groups is the formation of 3,5-bis(chloromethyl)-2-hydroxyacetophenone from 2-hydroxyacetophenone by carrying out the reaction with formaldehyde and hydrogen chloride at reflux temperature.[6] At 25–30° the monochloromethyl compound, 5-chloromethyl-2-hydroxyacetophenone, is obtained.

$$\text{ClCH}_2\text{—}\overset{\text{COCH}_3}{\underset{\underset{\text{CH}_2\text{Cl}}{\text{OH}}}{}} \xleftarrow[\text{HCl, CH}_2\text{O}]{\text{reflux}} \overset{\text{COCH}_3}{\underset{\text{OH}}{}} \xrightarrow[\text{HCl, CH}_2\text{O}]{25\text{–}30°} \text{ClCH}_2\text{—}\overset{\text{COCH}_3}{\underset{\text{OH}}{}}$$

On the basis of rate studies involving the chloromethylation of mesitylene the following mechanism was suggested.[7]

$$\text{CH}_2\text{O} + \text{H}^+ \rightleftharpoons \overset{+}{\text{C}}\text{H}_2\text{OH}$$

$$\text{ArH} + \overset{+}{\text{C}}\text{H}_2\text{OH} \longrightarrow \text{ArCH}_2\text{OH} + \text{H}^+$$

$$\text{ArCH}_2\text{OH} + \text{HCl} \rightleftharpoons \text{ArCH}_2\text{Cl} + \text{H}_2\text{O}$$

The rate-determining step is the electrophilic attack by $\overset{+}{\text{C}}\text{H}_2\text{OH}$. The results are consistent with the effect of substituents on the aromatic nucleus; electron-releasing groups facilitate the reaction, and with electron-withdrawing groups the reverse is true.

The chloromethylation procedure is a general one and is a valuable synthetic tool, inasmuch as the CH_2Cl group can be converted to other groups such as CH_3, CH_2CN, CHO, CH_2NH_2, and CH_2OH.

References

1. G. Blanc, *Bull. soc. chim. Paris* **33**, 313 (1923).
2. R. C. Fuson and C. H. McKeever, *in* "Organic Reactions" (R. Adams, ed.), Vol. I, p. 63. Wiley, New York, 1942.
3. O. Grummitt and A. Buck, *in* "Organic Syntheses" (N. L. Drake, ed.), Vol. 24, p. 30. Wiley, New York, 1944.
4. F. O. Cockerille, U. S. Patent 2,541,408 (Feb. 13, 1951); *Chem. Abstr.* **45**, 6662 (1951).
5. R. Andrisano, *Ann. chim. (Rome)* **40**, 30 (1950); *Chem. Abstr.* **45**, 7563 (1951).
6. R. Trave, *Gazz. chim. ital.* **80**, 502 (1950); *Chem. Abstr.* **45**, 7047 (1951).
7. Y. Ogata and M. Okane, *J. Am. Chem. Soc.* **78**, 5423 (1956).

Bouveault-Blanc[1] Reduction

Louis Bouveault (1864–1909) was born in Nevers, France. His life was devoted to teaching and to working in science. He received the Doctor of Science degree in 1890 from the Faculty of Medicine at Paris. Bouveault served on the faculties at Lyons, Lille, Nancy, and Paris. In 1907, he was president of the French Chemical Society. Although he died at a rather early age, Bouveault published a very large number of papers. One of his main interests was in the terpene field.

The reduction of esters to the corresponding alcohols by means of metallic sodium and ethyl alcohol was reported in 1903 by Bouveault and Blanc.[2] The method involves refluxing a solution of the ester in ethyl alcohol in the presence of an excess of sodium.

$$R{-}COOR' \xrightarrow[\text{Na}]{C_2H_5OH} R{-}CH_2OH + R'OH$$

Butyl alcohol has been employed in some instances to provide a higher refluxing temperature.

In 1947, Hansley[3] reported an improved method for reducing esters by means of metallic sodium. According to his proposed mechanism,[4] theoretical amounts of both sodium and reducing alcohol are required in the reduction. The reaction is carried out by the rapid addition of a mixture of the ester and reducing alcohol to the stirred molten sodium, alone, or in an inert solvent such as toluene or xylene.

Darzens[5] has reported a new general method of preparation of alcohols by reduction of acids, esters, ketones, and aldehydes with sodium hydride. The use of lithium aluminum hydride as the reducing agent offers a very convenient method for converting esters to alcohols.[6] Catalytic hydrogenation of esters to alcohols has been reviewed by Adkins.[7]

27

References

1. For G. Blanc's biography, see p. 24.
2. L. Bouveault and G. Blanc, *Compt. rend. acad. sci.* **136**, 1676 (1903); *Compt. rend. acad. sci.* **137**, 60, 328 (1903); *Bull. soc. chim. Paris* **31**, 666, 1203 (1904).
3. V. L. Hansley, *Ind. Eng. Chem.* **39**, 55 (1947).
4. See also L. Palfray and P. Anglaret, *Compt. rend. acad. sci.* **223**, 860 (1946).
5. G. Darzens, *Compt. rend. acad. sci.* **224**, 570 (1947).
6. For reductions by lithium aluminum hydride, see W. G. Brown, *in* "Organic Reactions" (R. Adams, ed.), Vol. VI, p. 469. Wiley, New York, 1951.
7. For a review of catalytic hydrogenation of esters to alcohols over a copper-chromic oxide or Raney nickel catalyst, see H. Adkins, *in* "Organic Reactions" (R. Adams, ed.), Vol. VIII, p. 1. Wiley, New York, 1954.

Bouveault Aldehyde Synthesis

The reaction of Grignard reagents with disubstituted formamides was shown by Bouveault[1] to give aldehydes.

$$RMgX + R'R''NCHO \longrightarrow RCHO + R'R''NH + MgX_2$$

The main side reaction in this synthesis is the formation of tertiary amines according to the following equation:

$$2RMgX + HCONR'R'' \longrightarrow R_2CHNR'R'' + MgO + MgX_2$$

Smith and co-workers[2,3] have investigated the use of Grignard reagents in the preparation of aldehydes. Using the Bouveault synthesis, they obtained a 50% yield of o-tolualdehyde from o-bromotoluene and N-methylformanilide.[1]

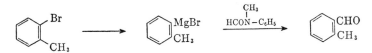

In a similar manner the *meta* and *para* isomers were prepared in 33% and 37% yield, respectively.

The reaction of Grignard reagents with an orthoformic ester is a more satisfactory method (*Bodroux-Tschitschibabin synthesis*) for the synthesis of aldehydes.

$$RMgX + HC(OR')_3 \longrightarrow RCH(OR')_2 + MgXOR'$$

$$RCH(OR')_2 + H_2O \xrightarrow{H^+} RCHO + 2R'OH$$

Smith and Nichols[3] showed that, when the mixture of Grignard reagent and ethyl orthoformate in ether was refluxed for five hours and the ether removed cautiously on the steam bath, a vigorous reaction occurred. The mixture was immediately cooled in an ice bath, and the reaction was allowed to proceed to completion. By this procedure they obtained o- and p-tolualdehyde from o- and p-bromotoluene in 74% and 73% yield, respectively. These yields are significantly higher than those obtained by the Bouveault synthesis.

Another illustration of the ethyl orthoformate procedure is the formation of caproaldehyde in 42% yield from amyl magnesium bromide.[4]

$$C_5H_{11}MgBr + CH(OC_2H_5)_3 \longrightarrow C_5H_{11}CH(OC_2H_5)_2 + C_2H_5OMgBr$$

$$C_5H_{11}CH(OC_2H_5)_2 \xrightarrow[H_2O]{H_2SO_4} C_5H_{11}CHO + 2C_2H_5OH$$

References

1. L. Bouveault, *Bull. soc. chim. Paris* **31**, 1306, 1322 (1904).
2. L. I. Smith and M. Bayliss, *J. Org. Chem.* **6**, 437 (1941).
3. L. I. Smith and J. Nichols, *J. Org. Chem.* **6**, 489 (1941).
4. C. A. Dornfeld and G. H. Coleman, *in* "Organic Syntheses" (H. R. Snyder, ed.), Vol. 28, p. 83. Wiley, New York, 1948.

Von Braun Reaction

Julius von Braun (1875–1940) was born in Warsaw, Poland. He studied at Munich, and Göttingen, where he received the Ph.D. degree in 1898 and later became an assistant professor. From 1909 to 1918, von Braun served as an associate professor at Breslau. In 1921 he joined the faculty at Frankfurt as professor of chemistry. Von Braun has published a large number of papers on a wide variety of subjects in organic chemistry. Many of these dealt with nitrogen heterocyclic compounds.

The von Braun reaction consists in the formation of a halide and benzonitrile by heating an N-substituted benzamide with phosphorus pentabromide or pentachloride. The reaction, which may be illustrated by the general equation

$$C_6H_5CONHR + PBr_5 \longrightarrow C_6H_5CN + RBr + POBr_3$$

is usually carried out by heating a mixture of the benzamide and pentahalide, and distilling the products. The method is a useful one for converting aliphatic amines to the corresponding halides because no rearrangement in R is brought about, in contrast to deamination with nitrous acid.

$$RNH_2 \xrightarrow{C_6H_5COCl} RNHCOC_6H_5 \xrightarrow{PX_5} RX$$

Dihalides may be prepared from cyclic amines. For example, with benzoylpiperidine,[1] 1,5-pentamethylene dibromide is obtained.

In a study on the mechanism of the von Braun reaction, Leonard and Nommensen[2] have shown that the reaction is inhibited by alkyl groups on the carbon atoms adjacent to the nitrogen. With N-benzoyl-2,2,6,6,-tetramethylpiperidine no dihalide was obtained. However, treatment of 1-benzoyl-2,5-bis(triphenylmethyl)-2,5-dihydropyrrole with phosphorus pentabromide gives 1,4-bis(triphenylmethyl)-1,2,3,4-tetra-bromobutane in 15% yield.[3]

References

1. J. von Braun, *Ber. deut. Chem. Ges.* **37**, 3210 (1904).
2. N. J. Leonard and E. W. Nommensen, *J. Am. Chem. Soc.* **71**, 2808 (1949).
3. J. B. Conant and B. C. Chow, *J. Am. Chem. Soc.* **55**, 3475 (1933).

Von Braun Degradation

A method of rupturing a C–N bond in a tertiary amine by reaction with cyanogen bromide is known as the von Braun degradation.[1] The bromine becomes attached to the carbon atom, and the cyano group to the nitrogen. An intermediate complex is probably involved which decomposes to give the cyanamide and alkyl bromide.

$$R_3N + BrCN \longrightarrow [R_3NCN]^+Br^- \longrightarrow R_2NCN + RBr$$

With unsymmetrical tertiary amines the products are determined by the nature of the substituents involved.

A study of the direction of ring opening in unsymmetrically substituted heterocycles has been reported by Elderfield.[2,3] With 1-butyl-2-methylpyrrolidine,[2] the reaction with cyanogen bromide in benzene gave two products, a primary and a secondary halide. When the reaction was carried out with 1-phenyl-2-methylpyrrolidine,[3] the proportion of primary and secondary halides was reversed. The presence of a phenyl group which reduces the basicity of the amine thus has a marked effect on the direction of ring cleavage.[4]

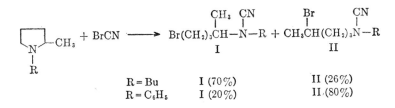

	I	II
R = Bu	I (70%)	II (26%)
R = C₆H₅	I (20%)	II (80%)

Another method of degradation of tertiary amines by spontaneous decomposition of quaternary acyloxyammonium salts into a carbinol amine is known as the *Polonovski reaction*.[5]

References

1. J. von Braun, *Ber. deut. Chem. Ges.* **33**, 1438 (1900).
2. R. C. Elderfield and H. A. Hageman, *J. Org. Chem.* **14**, 605 (1949).
3. R. C. Elderfield and M. Green, *J. Org. Chem.* **17**, 431 (1952).
4. A review of the von Braun cyanogen bromide reaction is given by H. A. Hageman *in* "Organic Reactions" (R. Adams, ed.), Vol. VII, p. 198. Wiley, New York, 1953.
5. See E. Wenkert, *Experientia* **10**, 346 (1954).

Bucherer Reaction

Hans Theodor Bucherer (1869–1949) was born in Ehrenfeld, Germany. He studied at Munich, Karlsruhe, and Leipzig, where he was a student of Wislicenus. After receiving his doctor's degree in 1893, Bucherer worked at the Badische Anilin und Soda-Fabrik at Ludwigshafen (1894–1900). He then became assistant professor at the Technische Hochschule at Dresden and, after several years, returned to industry to become director of a chemical factory in Berlin. In 1926, he was appointed professor of chemical technology at the Technische Hochschule at Munich.

One of Bucherer's main interests in chemistry was in aromatic diazonium compounds and their use in dyestuff manufacture.

Bucherer's brother, Alfred, was professor of theoretical physics at the University of Bonn.

The replacement of an amino group by an hydroxyl group by means of aqueous sulfite or bisulfite is commonly known as the Bucherer reaction.[1] Although the reaction had been reported previously, the general nature of the reaction and the fact that it is reversible were first demonstrated by Bucherer in 1904.[2] The reverse reaction is performed by heating with aqueous ammonia and ammonium sulfite.

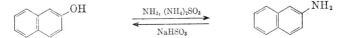

The preparation of 1-naphthol-4-sulfonic acid from naphthionic acid is an example in which an alpha-substituent is involved.

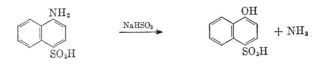

The Bucherer reaction, which has been used extensively in the naphthalene series, is of considerable importance in the preparation of dye intermediates. With the exception of resorcinol and phloroglucinol, the reaction is not applicable in the benzene series. The 6- and 8-hydroxyquinolines have been converted to the corresponding amines[3] by this method.

The mechanism of the Bucherer reaction is believed to involve the bisulfite addition compound (I) which probably results from the addition of bisulfite to the keto form of the naphthol.

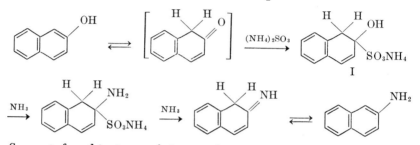

Support for this type of intermediate is given by Cowdrey and Hinshelwood,[4] who showed that the formation of the addition product is the rate-determining step in the reaction. An explanation of the formation of a dinaphthylamine as a by-product in the conversion of naphthylamines to naphthols is also reported.

Evidence has been presented[5] which indicates that the structure of the addition product of an α-naphthol with bisulfite is a tetrahydro-4-oxo-2-naphthalenesulfonic acid.

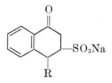

References

1. A review of the Bucherer reaction is given by N. L. Drake, in "Organic Reactions" (R. Adams, ed.), Vol. I, p. 105. Wiley, New York, 1942.
2. H. T. Bucherer, J. prakt. Chem. 69, 49 (1904).
3. N. N. Wonoshtzow and J. M. Kogan, Ber. deut. Chem. Ges. 65, 142 (1932).
4. W. A. Cowdrey and C. N. Hinshelwood, J. Chem. Soc. p. 1036 (1946); W. A. Cowdrey, J. Chem. Soc. pp. 1044, 1046 (1946).
5. A. Reiche and H. Seeboth, Angew. Chem. 70, 312 (1958).

Bucherer Hydantoin Synthesis

The formation of hydantoins by the interaction of a carbonyl compound with hydrogen cyanide (NaCN or KCN) and ammonium carbonate is known as the Bucherer hydantoin synthesis.[1,2]

$$R_2CO \xrightarrow[\text{HCN}]{\text{(NH}_4)_2\text{CO}_3} R_2C \underset{CO-NH}{\overset{NH-CO}{<}}$$

A mechanism for this reaction was proposed by Bucherer[1] involving an α-aminonitrile which could be formed from the cyanohydrin.

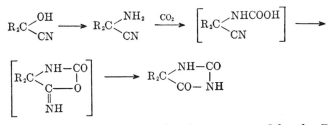

A large variety of hydantoins has been prepared by the Bucherer method as possible anticonvulsants. Henze and Leslie[3] have reported on the synthesis of some 5-benzohydryl-5-substituted-hydantoins.

$$(C_6H_5)_2CH \underset{R}{\overset{}{>}} C \underset{CO-NH}{\overset{NH-CO}{<}}$$

Bucherer studied the possibility of preparing dithiohydantoins by an extension of his method, but apparently without success. Carrington[4] showed that 5,5-disubstituted 2,4-dithiohydantoins can be prepared by the reaction of a ketone with carbon disulfide and ammonium cyanide in refluxing aqueous methyl alcohol.

$$R_2CO \xrightarrow[\text{CS}_2]{\substack{\text{NH}_4\text{Cl} \\ \text{NaCN}}} R_2C \underset{CS-NH}{\overset{NH-CS}{<}}$$

37

By treatment of the 2,4-dithiohydantoin with ammonia or primary amino compounds, the corresponding 4-imino derivative was obtained which on acid hydrolysis yielded the 5,5-disubstituted 2-thiohydantoin.[5]

$$R_2C \Big\langle \begin{matrix} NH-CS \\ | \\ CS-NH \end{matrix} \xrightarrow{NH_2CH_2CH_2OH} R_2C \Big\langle \begin{matrix} NH-CS \\ | \\ C-NH \\ \| \\ NCH_2CH_2OH \end{matrix} + H_2S \xrightarrow{H^+} R_2C \Big\langle \begin{matrix} NH-CS \\ | \\ CO-NH \end{matrix}$$

Pyridine aldehydes have been used in the preparation of 5-(α-,β-, and γ-pyridyl)hydantoins.[6] In the case of 2-pyridinecarboxaldehyde an oxazole intermediate was isolated.

References

1. H. T. Bucherer and W. Steiner, *J. prakt. Chem.* [2] **140**, 291 (1934).
2. H. T. Bucherer and V. A. Lieb, *J. prakt. Chem.* [2] **141**, 5 (1934).
3. H. R. Henze and W. B. Leslie, *J. Org. Chem.* **15**, 901 (1950); see also, H. R. Henze and W. C. Craig, *J. Org. Chem.* **10**, 2 (1945), for previous references.
4. H. C. Carrington. *J. Chem. Soc.* p. 681 (1947).
5. H. C. Carrington, *J. Chem. Soc.* p. 684 (1947).
6. M. Viscontini and H. Raschig, *Helv. Chim. Acta* **42**, 570 (1959).

Camps Reaction

Rudolf Camps worked under Professor Engler at the Technische Hochschule at Karlsruhe from 1899 to 1902. (Unfortunately, the archives of the University were destroyed by fire in 1944 so that no other information could be obtained.)

The formation of hydroxyquinolines by the intramolecular condensation of *o*-acylaminoacetophenones is referred to as the Camps reaction.[1] The reaction, which is base-catalyzed, may be illustrated by the formation of 2-hydroxy-4-methyl- and 4-hydroxy-2-methylquinoline from *o*-acetaminoacetophenone.

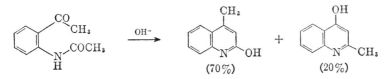

An unusual example of the Camps reaction has been reported by Koelsch and Lucht.[2] It involves the ring closure of 1-(carbethoxyacetamido)xanthone (I) with sodium ethoxide in ethyl alcohol to give the quinoline derivative (II).

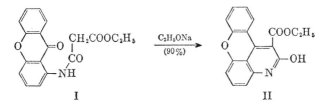

A new type of Camps reaction has recently been reported[3] in which the lactam (III) is converted to 2,3-cyclopentano-4-hydroxyquinoline (IV).

39

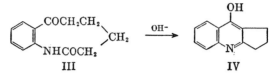

III   IV

The use of infrared and ultraviolet absorption spectra for distinguishing between 2- and 4-hydroxyquinolines is also reported in this work.

References

1. R. Camps, *Ber. deut. Chem. Ges.* **32**, 3228 (1899).
2. C. F. Koelsch and F. J. Lucht, *J. Am. Chem. Soc.* **71**, 3556 (1949).
3. B. Witkop, J. B. Patrick, and M. Rosenblum, *J. Am. Chem. Soc.* **73**, 2641 (1951).

Cannizzaro Reaction

Stanislao Cannizzaro (1826–1910) was born in Palermo, Italy. He studied under Professor Piria at Pisa, where his interest in chemistry was aroused. In 1847, Cannizzaro joined in the rebellion in Sicily and two years later escaped to Paris, where he resumed his work in chemistry. In 1851, he became professor at the National School of Alexandria, where he discovered benzyl alcohol which he obtained by the action of potassium hydroxide on benzaldehyde. In 1855 he became professor of chemistry at Genoa University, and six years later he was appointed professor at Palermo. In 1871, Cannizzaro assumed the chair of chemistry at Rome, which he held until his death.

For his outstanding work on the distinction between and determination of atomic and molecular weights, Cannizzaro received the Copley Medal from the Royal Society in 1891. These contributions to the atomic theory are recorded in the history of chemistry.

Cannizzaro entered the Italian Senate in 1871 and later became its vice-president.

The disproportionation of two molecules of an aldehyde (usually aromatic) brought about by the action of sodium or potassium hydroxide to yield the corresponding alcohol and acid is known as the Cannizzaro reaction.[1] The conversion of benzaldehyde into a mixture of benzyl alcohol and benzoic acid is an example.

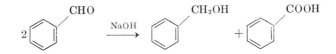

The formation of benzoic acid when benzaldehyde is treated with aqueous alkali was first observed by Wöhler and Liebig.[2] Some years later Cannizzaro[3] showed that benzyl alcohol is also formed.

The crossed Cannizzaro reaction in which the aldehyde is reduced by formaldehyde to yield the corresponding alcohol is applicable to a wide variety of compounds.

The reaction has been coupled with the Mannich reaction for the preparation of 2,2-dimethyl-3-(4-morpholinyl)-1-propanol and analogous amino alcohols.[4]

$R_2NH \cdot HCl + (CH_2O)_x + CH(CH_3)_2CHO \longrightarrow R_2NCH_2C(CH_3)_2CHO \xrightarrow[CH_3OH-KOH]{CH_2O}$

$R_2NCH_2C(CH_3)_2CH_2OH$

The mechanism of the reaction is the subject of a publication by Pfeil.[5] The effect of solvents, salts, and various metal hydroxides on the velocity constants of the Cannizzaro reaction was investigated, and the results showed that the weaker bases are more effective than sodium or potassium hydroxide. The best catalyst, according to this work, is calcium hydroxide. Pfeil assumed that initially a complex of two moles of the aldehyde and one mole of the metal hydroxide is formed, and that the hydrogen of one aldehyde group migrates as an anion to a neighboring carbon atom. The addition of the hydroxyl group to the

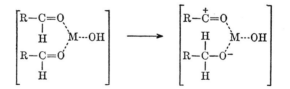

positive carbon atom gives rise to an acid and an alcohol. This addition of a hydrogen anion (hydride ion) to a carbonyl group also appears in the mechanism proposed by Hammett.[6]

α-Naphthyl carbinol and 5-methylfuryl carbinol have been prepared recently by crossed Cannizzaro reactions from the corresponding aldehydes.[7] The preparation of these alcohols by this procedure is more satisfactory than by other methods.

References

1. A review of the Cannizzaro reaction is given by T. A. Geissman, *in* "Organic Reactions" (R. Adams, ed.), Vol. II, p. 94. Wiley, New York, 1944.
2. F. Wöhler and J. Liebig, *Ann. Chem. Liebigs* **3**, 249 (1832).
3. S. Cannizzaro, *Ann. Chem. Liebigs* **88**, 129 (1853).
4. L. C. Cheney, *J. Am. Chem. Soc.* **73**, 685 (1951).
5. E. Pfeil, *Ber. deut. Chem. Ges.* **84**, 229 (1951).
6. L. Hammett, "Physical Organic Chemistry" p. 350. McGraw-Hill, New York, 1940; see also, E. R. Alexander, *J. Am. Chem. Soc.* **70**, 2592 (1948).
7. R. D. Tiwari and N. P. Srivastava, *Rec. trav. chim.* **75**, 254 (1956).

Chugaev Reaction

Leo Alexandrovitsch Chugaev (1873–1922) was born in Moscow, Russia. He was graduated from the University of Moscow, where he became an assistant in the Bacteriological Institute. Chugaev taught at the Technical High School of Moscow, and in 1908 he was appointed professor of inorganic chemistry at Petrograd, a position which had been held by Mendelejeff and Walden.

Chugaev's work in terpene chemistry led to his discovery of a new process for converting alcohols into olefins. He did a considerable amount of work in the field of complex compounds and showed that cyclic complex compounds are more stable than the corresponding acyclic compounds. He discovered the nickel derivative of dimethylglyoxime which is a valuable reagent in analytical chemistry.

The conversion of an alcohol to an olefin by the thermal decomposition of the methyl xanthate of the alcohol is known as the Chugaev reaction.[1]

$$RR'CHCH_2OH \xrightarrow[CS_2]{NaOH} RR'CHCH_2O\overset{\overset{S}{\|}}{C}-SNa \xrightarrow{CH_3I}$$

$$RR'CHCH_2O\overset{\overset{S}{\|}}{C}-SCH_3 \xrightarrow{\Delta T} RR'C=CH_2$$

A study of the mechanism of the Chugaev reaction has been reported by Alexander and Mudrack.[2] The absence of any rearrangements occurring during the dehydration process has been explained in terms of a cyclic transition state.

With the two racemate series of 3-phenyl-2-butanol, Cram[3] has shown that the Chugaev reaction proceeds for the most part in a stereospecific manner. The reaction is predominantly a *cis* elimination.

44

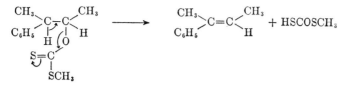

Bordwell and Landis[4] have recently shown that the acidity of the β-hydrogen eliminated in the reaction plays an important role in the course of the reaction. They have reported that pyrolysis of *cis-2-p-*tolylsulfonylcyclohexyl S-methyl xanthate (I) gave almost exclusively 1-*p*-tolylsulfonyl-1-cyclohexene (II) by a *trans* elimination. This is an exception to the usual *cis* elimination in the Chugaev reaction. The conformation is apparently not favorable for a cyclic mechanism.

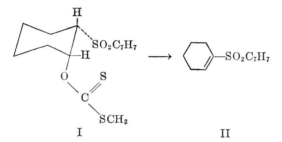

The same product II was also obtained by a *cis* elimination of the *trans* isomer of I.

References

1. L. Chugaev, *Ber. deut. Chem. Ges.* **32**, 3332 (1894).
2. E. R. Alexander and A. Mudrack, *J. Am. Chem. Soc.* **73**, 59 (1951).
3. D. J. Cram, *J. Am. Chem. Soc.* **71**, 3883 (1949).
4. F. G. Bordwell and P. S. Landis, *J. Am. Chem. Soc.* **80**, 2450 (1958).

Claisen Condensation

Rainer Ludwig Claisen (1851–1930) was born in Cologne, Germany. He studied under Kekulé at the University of Bonn, and later for a short time in Wöhler's laboratory at Göttingen. He returned to Bonn where he received his doctorate and became an assistant to Kekulé. Claisen then went to Owens College, Manchester, England, where he remained for about four years. From there he returned to Germany (1886) to work under von Baeyer at Munich. In 1890, he was appointed professor of chemistry at the Technische Hochschule at Aachen. Seven years later he joined the faculty at Kiel, and from there went to Berlin where he worked with Emil Fischer.

Claisen was a very skillful and prolific chemist; an organic chemist searching in the literature will invariably come upon some of Claisen's work. His accomplishments include work on the acylation of carbonyl compounds, the allyl rearrangement, the preparation of cinnamic acids, the synthesis of pyrazole and isoxazole derivatives, and the preparation of hydroxymethylene derivatives of acetoacetic and malonic esters.

The condensation of an ester with an active methylene compound (esters, aldehydes, ketones, nitriles) in the presence of a basic catalyst is usually referred to as a Claisen condensation. It is also known as the Claisen acylation, since it may be regarded essentially as an acylation of an active methylene compound. The preparation of ethyl acetoacetate[1] by the self-condensation of ethyl acetate in the presence of sodium ethoxide is a classical example.

$$2CH_3COOC_2H_5 \xrightarrow{\text{NaOC}_2\text{H}_5} CH_3COCH_2COOC_2H_5$$

The condensation most probably involves (a) the formation of an enolate ion by removal of a proton from the methylene group which

(b) reacts with a carbonyl group. The product loses an ethoxide ion to give a β-keto ester (c). If the β-keto ester has an α-hydrogen, it will in turn react (d) to give the enolate. Thus one mole of alkoxide is consumed.

(a) $CH_3COOC_2H_5 + B \rightleftharpoons \bar{C}H_2COOC_2H_5 + BH^+$

(b) $\bar{C}H_2COOC_2H_5 + CH_3\underset{\overset{\|}{O}}{C}OC_2H_5 \rightleftharpoons CH_3\underset{\overset{|}{O^-}}{\overset{\overset{OC_2H_5}{|}}{C}}-CH_2COOC_2H_5$

(c) $CH_3\underset{\overset{|}{O^-}}{\overset{\overset{OC_2H_5}{|}}{C}}-CH_2COOC_2H_5 \rightleftharpoons CH_3\underset{\overset{\|}{O}}{C}-CH_2COOC_2H_5 + C_2H_5O^-$

(d) $CH_3COCH_2COOC_2H_5 \xrightarrow{C_2H_5O^-} [CH_3COCHCOOC_2H_5]^- + C_2H_5OH$

With phenylacetonitrile and ethyl acetate the product is α-phenylacetoacetonitrile.[2]

$C_6H_5CH_2CN + CH_3COOC_2H_5 \xrightarrow[(73\%)]{NaOC_2H_5} C_6H_5CH(CN)COCH_3 + C_2H_5OH$

The condensation of phenylacetonitrile with ethyl oxalate in the presence of sodium ethoxide gives ethylphenylcyanopyruvate in 75% yield.[3]

$C_6H_5CH_2CN + \underset{\overset{|}{COOC_2H_5}}{\overset{\overset{COOC_2H_5}{|}}{}} \longrightarrow C_6H_5CH(CN)COCOOC_2H_5 + C_2H_5OH$

For the most part the catalysts employed in the Claisen condensation have been metallic sodium, sodium alkoxides, and sodium amide. Swamer and Hauser[4] investigated the use of sodium hydride in the Claisen acylation and carbethoxylation reactions. They found that this catalyst is as effective as other condensing agents and in many instances is superior to them. In the acylation of ketones with esters using sodium hydride the yields were as good as those obtained with sodium amide, and better than with sodium or sodium alkoxide. With acetone and ethyl laurate, for example, these investigators obtained an 83% yield of lauroylacetone.

$CH_3COCH_3 + C_{11}H_{23}COOC_2H_5 \xrightarrow{NaH} CH_3COCH_2COC_{11}H_{23}$

47

In the self-condensation of esters, sodium hydride is superior to the other condensing agents.

Claisen Reaction: A modification of the Perkin reaction (p. 184) for the preparation of β-arylacrylic acids, using sodium as the catalyst, is usually referred to as the Claisen reaction.[5] An illustration is the synthesis of ethyl β-phenylacrylate from benzaldehyde and ethyl acetate in the presence of metallic sodium and a trace of alcohol.

$$C_6H_5CHO + CH_3COOC_2H_5 \xrightarrow{Na} C_6H_5CH=CHCOOC_2H_5 + H_2O$$

References

1. For a review of the Claisen acetoacetic ester condensation and related reactions, see C. R. Hauser and B. E. Hudson, *in* "Organic Reactions" (R. Adams, ed.), Vol. I, p. 266. Wiley, New York, 1942.
2. P. L. Julian, J. J. Oliver, R. H. Kimball, A. B. Pike, and G. D. Jefferson, *in* "Organic Syntheses" (A. H. Blatt, ed.), Coll. Vol. II, p. 487. Wiley, New York, 1943.
3. R. Adams and H. O. Calvery, *in* "Organic Syntheses" (A. H. Blatt, ed.), Coll. Vol. II, p. 287. Wiley, New York, 1943.
4. F. W. Swamer and C. R. Hauser, *J. Am. Chem. Soc.* **72**, 1352 (1950).
5. See J. R. Johnson, *in* "Organic Reactions" (R. Adams, ed.), pp. 233–236. Wiley, New York, 1942.

Claisen Rearrangement

The migration of an allyl or substituted allyl group in allyl ethers of enols or phenols to give C-allyl derivatives is called the Claisen rearrangement.[1] This rearrangement, which occurs when an allyl ether is heated, is illustrated by the conversion of I → II and III → IV.

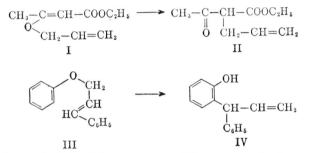

By distilling ethyl O-allylacetoacetate (I) at atmospheric pressure in the presence of ammonium chloride, Claisen[2] obtained the C-allyl compound (II). In the rearrangement of an allyl phenyl ether, no catalyst is necessary. The γ-carbon in the system (V) becomes attached to the carbon atom on the aromatic nucleus with a shift of the double bond from the β,γ position to the α,β position.

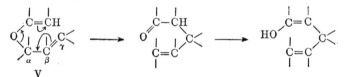

This migration of the double bond is demonstrated in the rearrangement III → IV[3] and with p-cresol allyl ether[4] containing C^{14}.

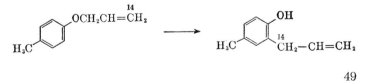

49

Retention of optical activity in the Claisen rearrangement has been reported[5] with optically active α,γ-dimethylallyl phenyl ether.

The allyl group usually migrates to the *ortho* position on the aromatic nucleus. However, if both *ortho* positions are substituted, rearrangement takes place to the *para* position. Ultraviolet irradiation of an isopropyl alcohol solution of allyl phenyl ether is reported to give *para* rearrangement.[6] In some instances, the Claisen rearrangement is accompanied by a displacement of an *ortho* substituent. This is especially true where one *ortho* substituent is a carboxyl group (VI → VII).

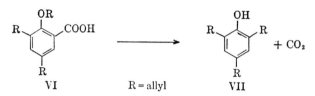

	R = allyl	
VI		VII

The Claisen rearrangement is especially useful in the synthesis of some naturally-occurring essential oils. By heating the rearranged product with strong alkali the double bond can be made to shift and become conjugated with the aromatic nucleus.

Phenyl allyl ether reacts with boron trichloride at −80° to form a product, which on hydrolysis gives exclusively o-allylphenol.[7]

Studies of the mechanism of the *para*-Claisen rearrangement have shown that allyl-cyclohexadienones are intermediates in the reaction.[8] Curtin and Crawford[9] have prepared 6-allyl-2,6-dimethyl-2,4-cyclo-hexadienone from the sodium salt of 2,6-dimethylphenol in benzene with allyl bromide. The dienone rearranges at temperatures above 70° to give a mixture of allyl 2,6-dimethylphenyl ether and 4-allyl-2,6-dimethylphenol.

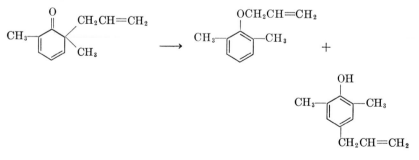

References

1. A review of the Claisen rearrangement is given by D. S. Tarbell, *in* "Organic Reactions" (R. Adams, ed.), Vol. II, p. 1. Wiley, New York, 1944.
2. L. Claisen, *Ber. deut. Chem. Ges.* **45**, 3157 (1912).
3. L. Claisen and E. Tietze, *Ber. deut. Chem. Ges.* **58**, 275 (1925).
4. H. Schmid and K. Schmid, *Helv. Chim. Acta* **35**, 1879 (1952).
5. E. R. Alexander and R. W. Kluiber, *J. Am. Chem. Soc.* **73**, 4304 (1951).
6. M. S. Kharasch, G. Stampa, and W. Nudenberg, *Science* **116**, 309 (1952).
7. W. Gerrard, M. F. Lappert, and H. B. Silver, *Proc. Chem. Soc.* p. 19 (1957).
8. See D. Y. Curtin and H. W. Johnson, *J. Am. Chem. Soc.* **78**, 2611 (1956).
9. D. Y. Curtin and R. J. Crawford, *J. Am. Chem. Soc.* **79**, 3156 (1957).

Claisen-Schmidt Condensation

Another reaction associated with Claisen is the Claisen-Schmidt condensation. It consists in the reaction of an aromatic aldehyde with an aliphatic aldehyde or ketone in the presence of aqueous alkali to form an α,β-unsaturated aldehyde or ketone. Benzylideneacetophenone may be prepared by this method in 85% yield from benzaldehyde and acetophenone.[1]

$$C_6H_5CHO + CH_3COC_6H_5 \xrightarrow{-H_2O} C_6H_5CH{=}CHCOC_6H_5$$

This product is also known under the name chalcone. Its derivatives have been the subject of wide investigation in connection with antibacterial activity. The antibiotic activity of the chalcones is attributed to their unsaturation, since saturation of the double bond results in a loss of activity. Some coumarones have recently been prepared for therapeutic evaluation.[2] For example, 2-(4-bromobenzoyl)-5-bromocoumarone has been synthesized from 5-bromosalicylaldehyde and 4-bromophenacyl bromide in alcoholic potassium hydroxide solution.

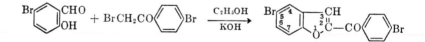

The Claisen-Schmidt reaction has been employed by Johnson[3] as part of a method for introducing an angular methyl group. The procedure involves the preparation of the benzylidene derivative of 1-decalone to protect the methylene group, methylation, and removal of the benzylidene group.

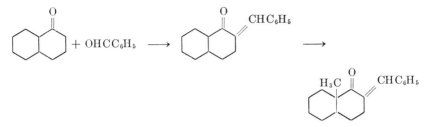

The preparation of β-nitrostyrenes by the reaction of nitroalkanes with aromatic aldehydes in the presence of alkali may be included under the Claisen-Schmidt condensation. The nitrostyrenes have been employed as intermediates in the preparation of β-phenethylamines, many of which have pharmacological activity, and which may also be used for the syntheses of isoquinolines. The preparation of β-(3-methoxy-4-benzyloxy)phenethylamine from the nitrostyrene (I) by reduction with lithium aluminum hydride is an example.[4]

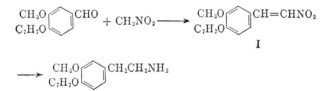

Davey and Tivey[5] have recently investigated the optimum conditions for the preparation of chalcones. The condensing agents, sodium hydroxide and sodium methoxide, were found to be generally more effective than hydrogen chloride, phosphorus oxychloride or boron trifluoride. These authors also studied the addition of hydrogen cyanide to chalcones, and the products obtained by hydrolysis of the adducts.

References

1. E. P. Kohler and H. M. Chadwell, in "Organic Syntheses" (A. H. Blatt, ed.), Coll. Vol. I, p. 71. Wiley, New York, 1941.
2. E. Schraufstätter and S. Deutsch, Z. Naturforsch. 4b, 276 (1949); Chem. Abstr. 44, 3568 (1950).
3. W. S. Johnson, J. Am. Chem. Soc. 65, 1317 (1943).
4. J. Finkelstein, J. Am. Chem. Soc. 73, 550 (1951).
5. W. Davey and D. J. Tivey, J. Chem. Soc. p. 1230 (1958).

Clemmensen Reduction

Erik Christian Clemmensen (1876–1941) was born in Odense, Denmark. He studied at the Royal Polytechnic Institute in Copenhagen, where he received the M.S. degree. In 1900, he came to the United States where he was employed as a research chemist by Parke, Davis and Company until 1914. During this period Clemmensen carried out his work on the reduction of carbonyl compounds with amalgamated zinc. After this work was published, he received the Ph.D. degree from the University of Copenhagen. Clemmensen was one of the founders (1914) of the Commonwealth Chemical Corporation, which was merged with the Mathieson Alkali Works, Inc., in 1923. Six years later, after a disastrous fire, the company was purchased by the Monsanto Chemical Company, and Clemmensen joined the research staff in the department headed by L. R. Kyrides. Some of his work there included the preparation of alkyl and aryl phosphates and thiophosphates. In 1933, he founded the Clemmensen Chemical Corporation in Newark, New York, and held the position of president of that company until his death.

The conversion of a carbonyl group to a methylene group by means of amalgamated zinc and hydrochloric acid is known as the Clemmensen method of reduction.[1,2] The method is applicable to a

$$\underset{R'}{\overset{R}{>}}C=O \quad \xrightarrow[\text{HCl}]{Zn(Hg)_x} \quad \underset{R'}{\overset{R}{>}}CH_2$$

wide variety of carbonyl compounds. It is especially useful in the synthesis of hydrocarbons from aliphatic aromatic ketones prepared via the Friedel-Crafts reaction. The reduction is usually carried out by refluxing the carbonyl compound with amalgamated zinc in an excess of hydrochloric acid. Solvents miscible and immiscible with hydrochloric acid have been employed.[2] An example of the reaction is the preparation of n-amylbenzene from phenyl n-butyl ketone.[3]

54

The yields of products by this method of reduction are usually satisfactory. Halogens as well as double bonds conjugated with the carbonyl group are reduced under the conditions of the Clemmensen method. The main side reaction is bimolecular reduction.

In an attempt to clarify the mechanism of the reaction the products from the reduction of acetophenone have been examined by gas chromatography.[4] The results indicate that acetophenone is reduced to ethylbenzene primarily by way of α-methylbenzyl alcohol and (1-chloroethyl)benzene.

$$C_6H_5COCH_3 \longrightarrow C_6H_5CHOHCH_3 \longrightarrow C_6H_5CHClCH_3 \longrightarrow$$
$$C_6H_5CH_2CH_3$$

Under Clemmensen conditions α-methylbenzyl alcohol itself is reduced to ethylbenzene. Another example of the reduction of an alcohol by means of zinc amalgam, and hydrochloric acid is the formation of 4-octanone from butyroin.[5]

$$C_3H_7COCHOHC_3H_7 \longrightarrow C_3H_7COCH_2C_3H_7$$

An interesting reaction involving the Clemmensen reduction is the ring enlargement of 1-methyl-2-propionylpyrrolidine (I) to 2-ethyl-1-methylpiperidine (II).[6]

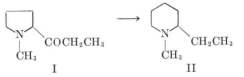

A molecular rearrangement during a Clemmensen reduction of 5,5-dimethyl-1,3-cyclohexanedione which results in ring contraction has been reported by Dey and Linstead.[7]

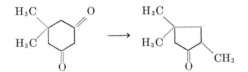

An extensive investigation of the rearrangement of α-amino ketones during Clemmensen reduction has been reported by Leonard.[8]

55

References

1. E. Clemmensen, *Ber. deut. Chem. Ges.* **46,** 1837 (1913); *Ber. deut. Chem. Ges.* **47,** 51 (1914).
2. A review of the Clemmensen reduction is presented by E. L. Martin, *in* "Organic Reactions" (R. Adams, ed.), Vol. I, p. 155. Wiley, New York, 1942.
3. H. A. Fahim and A. Mustafa, *J. Chem. Soc.* p. 519 (1949).
4. M. Poutsma and E. Wolthius, *J. Org. Chem.* **24,** 875 (1959); see also, D. Staschewski, *Angew. Chem.* **71,** 726 (1959).
5. W. T. Smith, *J. Am. Chem. Soc.* **73,** 1883 (1951).
6. G. R. Clemo and J. J. Vipond, *Chem. & Ind. (London)* p. 856 (1949); R. R. Clemo, R. Raper, and H. J. Vipond, *J. Chem. Soc.* p. 2095 (1949).
7. A. N. Dey and R. P. Linstead, *J. Chem. Soc.* p. 1063 (1935).
8. See, N. J. Leonard and E. D. Nicholaides, *J. Am. Chem. Soc.* **73,** 5210 (1951).

Combes Quinoline Synthesis

Alphonse-Edmond Combes (1858–1896) was born in St. Hippolyte-du-Fort, France. He studied under Wurtz at Paris, where he later became a lecturer. Combes was particularly interested in reactions with aluminum chloride. He synthesized acetylacetone by the reaction of aluminum chloride with acetyl chloride, and studied its properties. He showed that aniline reacts with acetylacetone with liberation of water, and that the product is converted by sulfuric acid to a dimethylquinoline. He also synthesized chloro derivatives of acetylacetone.

In collaboration with Charles Friedel, Combes studied the action of phenylhydrazine on camphoric anhydride, and the synthesis of pyrazoles.

Combes was president of the French Chemical Society in 1893. His sudden death, soon after his thirty-eighth birthday, came as a shock to all who knew him.

The condensation of arylamines with 1,3-diketones followed by ring closure of the product with concentrated sulfuric acid to yield quinoline derivatives is known as the Combes synthesis.[1,2] The synthesis is a general one. With aniline and acetylacetone the product is 2,4-dimethylquinoline.

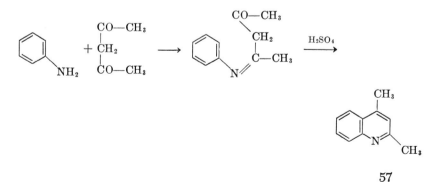

According to Roberts and Turner,[3] cyclization proceeds readily with a strongly *ortho-para* orienting group in the *meta* position to the nitrogen atom. Similar groups in the *para* position inhibit the ring closure. Nitroanilines do not react in the Combes synthesis. The product with *meta*-substituted anilines is predominately the 7-substituted quinoline. For example, from *m*-chloroaniline, 7-chloro-2,4-dimethylquinoline is obtained.[3] In the Skraup reaction (p. 218) both the 5- and 7-chloroquinolines are formed.

Johnson and Mathews[4] have investigated the products obtained in the Combes reaction with β-naphthylamine. The condensation with acetylacetone in the presence of Drierite gave an 83% yield of the

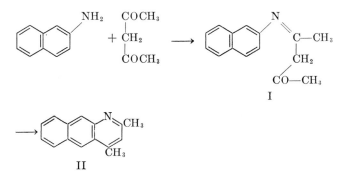

anil I. Cyclization with concentrated sulfuric acid at 60°, or better with anhydrous hydrogen fluoride, gave the linear compound 2,4-dimethylbenzo[g]quinoline (II). The expected angular isomer was obtained in small yield by ring closure of the anil (I) with concentrated sulfuric acid at steam bath temperature.

References

1. A. Combes, *Bull. soc. chim. Paris* **49**, 89 (1888); *Compt. rend. acad. sci.* **106**, 142, 1536 (1888).
2. R. C. Elderfield, ed., *in* "Heterocyclic Compounds," Vol. 4, pp. 36–37. Wiley, New York, 1952.
3. E. Roberts and E. E. Turner, *J. Chem. Soc.* p. 1832 (1927).
4. W. S. Johnson and F. J. Mathews, *J. Am. Chem. Soc.* **66**, 210 (1944).

Conrad-Limpach Synthesis

Max Conrad (1848–1920) was born in Munich, Germany. He received the Ph.D. degree in 1875 from the University of Würzburg, where he was appointed assistant professor. Later he became professor of chemistry and mineralogy at the Forest Academy in Aschaffenburg. Conrad was interested in the chemistry of barbituric, cyanoacetic, and malonic acid derivatives.

* * *

Leonhard Limpach (1852–1933) was born at Schweinfurt, Germany. He studied at Würzburg and became a pharmacist. He continued his studies under Wislicenus and then went to work in an English dyestuff company. Limpach returned to Germany in 1895, opened a pharmacy, and lectured at Erlangen on pharmacy. After World War I, he returned to the university.

Limpach is probably best known for his work with Conrad on the synthesis of quinoline derivatives. He was also interested in problems related to the dye industry.

The Conrad-Limpach synthesis[1,2] consists in the preparation of 4-hydroxyquinolines starting with an arylamine and a β-keto ester. The reactions involved in the synthesis may be illustrated by the preparation of 7-chloro-4-hydroxyquinoline.[3]

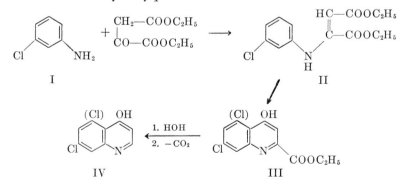

Diethyl oxalacetate is condensed with *m*-chloroaniline to give the intermediate (II) which is cyclized by pyrolysis in Dowtherm at about 245°. Both the 5- and 7-chloro-4-hydroxyquinaldic acid esters (III) are obtained. Increasing the amount of solvent in the cyclization step appears to have no appreciable effect upon the yield and ratio of isomers formed.[4] The isomeric esters are separated by fractional recrystallization and hydrolyzed. The resulting acids are decarboxylated by heating in Dowtherm at 210°. The 4-hydroxyquinolines have been used as intermediates in the synthesis of antimalarial drugs.

The reaction of the arylamine with a β-keto ester can proceed in either of two ways, formation of an anil or an anilide. In the latter case a 2-hydroxyquinoline may be obtained (*Knorr synthesis*[5]).

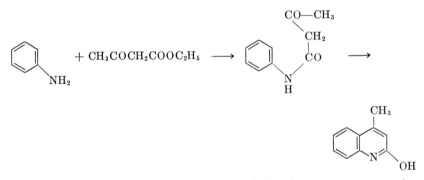

Hauser and Reynolds[6] have investigated the factors governing the formation of anils and anilides. The reactions are reversible, and the anil may be converted to the anilide by heating at 130–140° with water and a trace of acid.

References

1. M. Conrad and L. Limpach, *Ber. deut. Chem. Ges.* **20**, 948 (1887).
2. R. H. Reitsma, *Chem. Revs.* **43**, 43 (1948); R. C. Elderfield, ed., *in* "Heterocyclic Compounds," Vol. 4, pp. 30–38. Wiley, New York, 1952.
3. A. R. Surrey and H. F. Hammer, *J. Am. Chem. Soc.* **68**, 113 (1946).
4. A. M. Spivey and F. H. S. Curd, *J. Chem. Soc.* p. 2656 (1949).
5. L. Knorr, *Ann. Chem. Liebigs* **236**, 69 (1886); *Ann. Chem. Liebigs* **245**, 357 (1888).
6. C. R. Hauser and G. A. Reynolds, *J. Am. Chem. Soc.* **70**, 2402 (1948).

Curtius Reaction

Theodor Curtius (1857–1928) was born in Duisburg, Germany. He studied chemistry under Bunsen at Heidelberg and under Kolbe at Leipzig, where he obtained his Ph.D. degree. Curtius then went to Munich, where he worked under von Baeyer, and from there he went to Erlangen. He was appointed professor of chemistry at Kiel and in 1901 succeeded Victor Meyer at Heidelberg.

Curtius discovered diazoacetic ester, hydrazine, and hydrazoic acid, and investigated the chemistry of these new compounds. This led to the synthesis of triazoles, tetrazoles, azines, hydrazones, and acid azides.

Curtius was also interested in music. He sang in concerts and composed music.

The Curtius reaction[1,2] refers to the preparation of primary amines from acid azides according to the following equation:

$$R-CON_3 \longrightarrow R-N=C=O \longrightarrow R-NH_2$$

The process offers an additional method to the Hofmann and Schmidt reactions[3] for replacing a carboxyl group by an amino group. The acid azide can be prepared either from the hydrazide with nitrous acid or from the acid chloride with sodium azide.

$$R-COOC_2H_5 \xrightarrow{NH_2NH_2} R-CONHNH_2 \xrightarrow{HONO} R-CON_3$$

$$R-COOH \longrightarrow R-COCl \xrightarrow{NaN_3} R-CON_3$$

The initial product formed in the decomposition of an acid azide is an isocyanate which can be isolated if the reaction is carried out in an inert solvent. Under other reaction conditions, products such as urethans, ureas, and amides are obtained.

A wide variety of acids have been employed in the Curtius reaction. Diamines are readily formed from dicarboxylic acids. Monohydrazides of dicarboxylic acids give amino acids. With α-hydroxy acid azides, aldehydes or ketones are obtained.

$$\underset{\overset{\displaystyle |}{OH}}{\overset{\overset{\displaystyle R'}{\displaystyle |}}{R-C}}-CON_3 \longrightarrow \overset{\overset{\displaystyle R'}{\displaystyle |}}{R-C}=O + HNCO$$

The urethane from a β-hydroxy acid isomerizes to give an oxazolidone. This novel reaction has been employed recently[4] for the preparation of some phenylethanolamines.

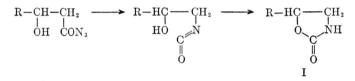

I

N-Methylation of the oxazolidone (I) followed by opening of the ring with hydrochloric acid gives $R-CHOH-CH_2NHCH_3$, where R is m- or p-hydroxyphenyl.

The mechanism of the Curtius reaction is usually represented as involving the intermediate (II), which is the same intermediate de-

$$\overset{\overset{\displaystyle O}{\displaystyle \|}}{R-C}-\overset{..}{\underset{..}{N}}-\overset{+}{N}\equiv N: \longrightarrow \overset{\overset{\displaystyle O}{\displaystyle \|}}{R-C}-\overset{..}{\underset{..}{N}} + N_2$$

II

scribed for the Hofmann and Lossen rearrangements. The formation of this radical is probably accompanied by the simultaneous migration of R with retention of configuration, to form the isocyanate.[5]

The effect of o-, m-, and p-substituents on the rate of the Curtius rearrangement of benzazides has been reported.[6] The rates of o-substituted derivatives were much greater than those for the m-, and p-derivatives. These results are attributed to a steric effect, particularly to a steric restriction of resonance.

References

1. T. Curtius *Ber. deut. Chem. Ges.* **23**, 3023 (1890); *J. prakt. Chem.* **50**, 275 (1894).

2. A review of the Curtius reaction is given by P. A. S. Smith, *in* "Organic Reactions" (R. Adams, ed.), Vol. III, p. 337. Wiley, New York, 1946.

3. A comparison of the Curtius, Hofmann, and Schmidt reactions is given by P. A. S. Smith, *in* "Organic Reactions" (R. Adams, ed.), Vol. III, p. 363. Wiley, New York, 1946.

4. E. D. Bergmann and M. Sulzbacher, *J. Org. Chem.* **16**, 84 (1951).

5. C. R. Hauser and S. W. Kantor, *J. Am. Chem. Soc.* **72**, 4284 (1950).

6. Y. Yukawa and Y. Tsuno, *J. Am. Chem. Soc.* **80**, 6346 (1958).

Dakin Reaction

Henry Drysdale Dakin (1880–1952) was born in London, England. He studied chemistry under Julius B. Cohen at the University of Leeds, where he received the Ph.D. degree in 1907. At the Lister Institute of Preventive Medicine, Dakin began his investigations which were to mark him as one of the leaders in the field of biochemistry. During World War I, he went to France where he developed his hypochlorite solution (Dakin's solution) for the treatment of wounds. Dakin continued his research in New York, and served as a scientific adviser to the Merck Institute for Therapeutic Research. He received many honors, including the Davy Medal of the Royal Society and honorary degrees from the Universities of Leeds, Heidelberg, and Yale.

Dakin discovered many enzymes. His studies on enzyme action led to the view of enzyme-substrate combination. Dakin is also well known for his studies on metabolism. He showed that amino acids were deaminated and decarboxylated by hydrogen peroxide, and he supplied experimental evidence for Knoop's β-oxidation of fatty acids. His interest in hydrogen peroxide oxidations led to the Dakin reaction. In 1928, Dakin and Randolph West, a clinician, reported on the reaction of α-amino acids with acetic anhydride and pyridine to give α-acylamino ketones.

When an alkaline solution of an *o*- or *p*-hydroxybenzaldehyde (or ketone) is treated with dilute hydrogen peroxide, a polyhydric phenol is formed.[1] In this manner, *p*-hydroxybenzaldehyde is converted to quinol.

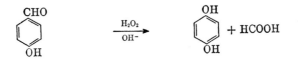

The Dakin reaction is especially useful in the preparation of poly-hydric phenols from naturally occurring hydroxyaldehydes. The reaction of o-vanillin with hydrogen peroxide in an inert atmosphere gives pyrogallol 1-monomethyl ether in 80% yield.[2]

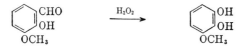

An illustration of the Dakin reaction in which a ketone is involved is the preparation of 3,4-dihydroxyphenylacetonitrile from 5-cyano-methyl-2-hydroxyacetophenone.[3]

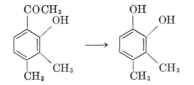

The oxidation of 2-hydroxy-3,4-dimethylacetophenone with hydro-gen peroxide in aqueous tetramethylammonium hydroxide solution gave a 25% yield of 3,4-dimethylcatechol.[4] In aqueous potassium

hydroxide solution the yield was only 2.5%. The yield in Triton B (benzyltrimethylammonium hydroxide) was 18%.

References

1. H. D. Dakin, Am. Chem. J. 42, 477 (1909).
2. A. R. Surrey, in "Organic Syntheses" (H. Adkins, ed.), Vol. 26, p. 90. Wiley, New York, 1946.
3. R. Trave, Gazz, chim. ital. 80, 502 (1950); Chem. Abstr. 45, 7047 (1951).
4. W. Baker, H. F. Bondy, J. Gump, and D. Miles, J. Chem. Soc. p. 1615 (1953).

Dakin-West Reaction

The reaction of α-amino acids with acetic anhydride in the presence of pyridine to give α-acetamidoalkyl methyl ketones was reported by Dakin and West in 1928.[1] An example is the preparation of 1-phenyl-2-acetamido-3-butanone from phenylalanine.

$$C_6H_5CH_2CH\text{—}COOH + (CH_3CO)_2O \longrightarrow$$
$$\underset{NH_2}{|}$$

$$C_6H_5CH_2CH\text{—}COCH_3 + CO_2 + H_2O$$
$$\underset{NHCOCH_3}{|}$$

In this reaction anhydrous sodium acetate has been used as the base.[2]

It has also been shown[2] that other anhydrides, such as propionic, butyric, and benzoic, may be successfully employed in the Dakin-West reaction. With phenylalanine and propionic anhydride the product is 1-phenyl-2-propionamido-3-pentanone.

$$C_6H_5CH_2CH\text{—}COOH + (CH_3CH_2CO)_2O \longrightarrow$$
$$\underset{NH_2}{|}$$

$$C_6H_5CH_2CH\text{—}COCH_2CH_3 + CO_2 + H_2O$$
$$\underset{NHCOCH_2CH_3}{|}$$

66

The mechanism of the Dakin-West reaction is believed to involve a base-catalyzed acylation of an oxazolone[2,3] which is similar to the Erlenmeyer reaction.

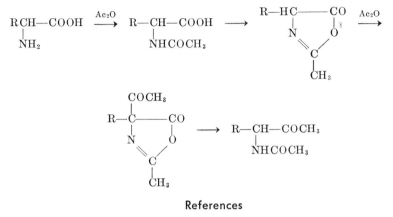

References

1. H. D. Dakin and R. West, *J. Biol. Chem.* **78**, 91, 745, 757 (1928).
2. G. H. Cleland and C. Niemann, *J. Am. Chem. Soc.* **71**, 841 (1949).
3. J. W. Cornforth and D. F. Elliot, *Science* **112**, 534 (1950).

Darzens Glycidic Ester Condensation

Georges Auguste Darzens (1867–1954) was born in Moscow, Russia. In 1895, he received the Doctor of Physical Science degree from the École Polytechnique in Paris, where he later became professor of chemistry. Darzens name is known for his contributions of the glycidic ester condensation, the syntheses of tetralin derivatives, and unsaturated ketones. One of his more recent interests was the investigation of the Walden inversion.

The condensation of an aldehyde or ketone with an α-halo ester in the presence of a basic condensing agent to give a glycidic ester is known as the Darzens glycidic ester condensation.[1,2] The reaction may be expressed by the following general equation:

$$RR'CO + XCHR''COOC_2H_5 \longrightarrow RR'C\overset{O}{\overset{\diagup\diagdown}{-}}CR''COOC_2H_5$$

Both aliphatic and aromatic aldehydes and ketones, and α-chloro and α-bromo esters have been employed in this condensation. The condensing agents are sodium amide, sodium, or a sodium alkoxide. The reaction is performed in an inert atmosphere by adding the condensing agent with cooling to a mixture of the carbonyl compound and α-halo ester. After a period of time, the reaction mixture is treated with dilute acid, and the desired product is extracted and purified by vacuum distillation.

The mechanism of the Darzens condensation is commonly described as follows:[3]

$$ClCH_2COOC_2H_5 + B \longrightarrow Cl\bar{C}HCOOC_2H_5 + BH^+$$

$$Cl\bar{C}HCOOC_2H_5 + RR'CO \longrightarrow RR'C\underset{O^-}{\overset{|}{-}}\underset{Cl}{\overset{|}{C}}HCOOC_2H_5 \longrightarrow$$

$$RR'C\overset{\diagup\diagdown}{\underset{O}{-}}CHCOOC_2H_5 + Cl^-$$

A variety of different types of compounds may be prepared from the glycidic ester. Hydrolysis of the glycidic ester to the glycidic acid, followed by decarboxylation, yields an aldehyde or ketone. The former is generally prepared by making $R'' = H$.

$$R-\underset{\underset{O}{\diagdown\diagup}}{\overset{\overset{R'\ \ R''}{|\ \ \ |}}{C-C}}-COOC_2H_5 \longrightarrow R-\underset{\underset{O}{\diagdown\diagup}}{\overset{\overset{R'\ \ R''}{|\ \ \ |}}{C-C}}-COOH \xrightarrow{\Delta T} R-\overset{\overset{R'}{|}}{C}HCOR''$$

For example, from ethyl β-methyl-β-phenylglycidate ($R = CH_3$, $R' = C_6H_5$, $R'' = H$), α-phenylpropionaldehyde is obtained in 70% yield.[4]

The Darzens glycidic ester condensation has been used starting with the Diels-Alder adduct from p-quinone and butadiene, for the

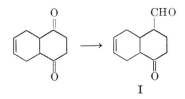

I

preparation of the keto-aldehyde I.[5] This intermediate was employed in the total synthesis of yohimbine.

Sodium $tert$-amyl oxide has proved to be an efficient catalyst for the condensation of ethyl β-benzoylpropionate with ethyl chloroacetate.[6] This is apparently the first example of a keto ester being used in the Darzens reaction.

References

1. G. Darzens, *Compt. rend. acad. sci.* **139**, 1214 (1904).
2. A review of the Darzens glycidic ester condensation is given by M. S. Newman and B. J. Magerlein, *in* "Organic Reactions" (R. Adams, ed.), Vol. V, p. 413. Wiley, New York, 1949.
3. A review of the mechanism of the Darzens and related condensations is given by M. Ballester, *Chem. Revs.* **55**, 283 (1955); see also, M. Ballester and D. Pérez-Blanco, *J. Org. Chem.* **23**, 652 (1958).
4. C. F. H. Allen and J. Van Allan, *in* "Organic Syntheses" (N. L. Drake, ed.), Vol. 24, p. 82. Wiley, New York, 1944.
5. E. E. van Tamelen, *J. Am. Chem. Soc.* **80**, 5006 (1958).
6. E. D. Bergmann, S. Yaroslavsky, and H. Weiler-Feilchenfeld, *J. Am. Chem. Soc.* **81**, 2775 (1959).

Darzens Synthesis of Unsaturated Ketones

In 1910, Darzens[1] reported a new general method of synthesizing unsaturated ketones by treating an ethylene compound with acetyl chloride in the presence of aluminum chloride. An illustration is the preparation of tetrahydroacetophenone from cyclohexene.

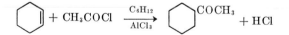

Aluminum chloride is added to the mixture of cyclohexene and acetyl chloride in carbon disulfide at 0°, and the chloro ketone thus formed is liberated by pouring the mixture into ice-water. On treatment with a tertiary base, such as diethylaniline, hydrogen chloride is evolved and tetrahydroacetophenone is obtained. The reaction is applicable to aliphatic and cyclic olefins. Other metallic halides such as $SnCl_4$, $FeCl_3$, and $SbCl_3$ may be used as the catalyst.

Nenitzescu[2] found that if cyclohexane is used as a solvent in the Darzens synthesis a saturated ketone is formed. For example, when aluminum chloride was added to a mixture of cyclohexene and acetyl chloride in cyclohexane at about −10° and the reaction mixture warmed to 70°, hydrogen chloride was evolved and methyl cyclohexyl ketone was obtained.

Apparently the unsaturated ketone is hydrogenated at the expense of the solvent.

With cycloheptene,[3] the *Nenitzescu reaction* gives a mixture of products.

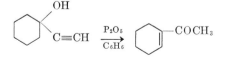

Nenitzescu[4] also found that when cyclohexene was added to acetyl chloride and aluminum chloride in carbon disulfide at $-15°$ and then benzene added, 1-phenyl-4-acetylcyclohexane was formed.[5]

The reaction probably involves a migration of the chlorine atom in the chloro ketone, followed by a Friedel-Crafts alkylation.

In a similar manner 4-phenyl-2-pentanone was prepared from propene.

$$CH_3CH{=}CH_2 \xrightarrow[C_6H_6,\ AlCl_3]{CH_3COCl} CH_3CH(C_6H_5)CH_2COCH_3$$

The same product is obtained from the unsaturated ketone with benzene and aluminum chloride.

$$CH_3CH{=}CHCOCH_3 \xrightarrow[AlCl_3]{C_6H_6} CH_3CH(C_6H_5)CH_2COCH_3$$

Solutions of carboxylic acids in trifluoroacetic anhydride have been used for the preparation of acyl olefins.[6] The unsymmetrical anhydride adds across the unsaturated bond at room temperatures. The initial product decomposes spontaneously to give the acyl olefin and trifluoroacetic acid.

$$RCOOCOCF_3 + R'CH{=}CH{-}R'' \longrightarrow RCOCHR'CHR''OCOCF_3 \longrightarrow$$
$$RCOCR'{=}CHR'' + CF_3COOH$$

Tetrahydroacetophenone has also been prepared by the *Meyer-Schuster rearrangement* of 1-ethynylcyclohexanol.[7]

71

References

1. G. Darzens, *Compt. rend. acad. sci.* **150**, 707 (1910).
2. C. D. Nenitzescu and E. Cioranescu, *Ber. deut. Chem. Ges.* **69**, 1820 (1936).
3. S. L. Friess and R. Pinson, *J. Am. Chem Soc.* **73**, 3512 (1951).
4. C. D. Nenitzescu and I. G. Gavăt, *Ann. Chem. Liebigs* **519**, 260 (1935).
5. See also W. S. Johnson and R. D. Offenhauer, *J. Am. Chem. Soc.* **67**, 1045 (1945).
6. A. L. Henne and J. M. Tedder, *J. Chem. Soc.* p. 3628 (1953).
7. J. H. Saunders, *in* "Organic Synthesis" (C. S. Hamilton, ed.), Vol. 29, p. 1. Wiley, New York, 1949.

Delépine Reaction

Marcel Delépine (1871–   ) was born in Saint Martin le Gaillard, France. His interests during his long, fruitful career in science included pharmacy, organic, and inorganic chemistry.

Delépine was an assistant to M. Bertholet at the Collège de France and later became a professor at that institution. His varied and prolific researches in organic chemistry include a study of catalytic hydrogenation with Raney nickel; the preparation of primary amines from benzyl halides via hexamethylenetetramine quaternary salts; investigation of a variety of sulfur compounds; and reactions in the terpene series.

Delépine is a past president of the French Chemical Society and an honorary member of several foreign chemical societies.

The acid hydrolysis of hexamethylenetetramine quaternary salts, prepared from benzyl or alkyl halides and hexamethylenetetramine, to give primary amines is known as the Delépine reaction.[1] In addition to the primary amine, formaldehyde and ammonium chloride are formed.

$$RCH_2X + C_6H_{12}N_4 \longrightarrow [RCH_2 \cdot C_6H_{12}N_4]^+X^-$$

$$[RCH_2 \cdot C_6H_{12}N_4]^+X^- + 3HCl + 6H_2O \longrightarrow RCH_2NH_2 \cdot HX + 6CH_2O + 3NH_4Cl$$

If alcohol is employed as a solvent in the hydrolysis, the acetal of formaldehyde is one of the products.

A simplified procedure for the Delépine reaction, which is an excellent general method for the preparation of primary amines, has been reported by Galat and Elion.[2] These authors employed 95% alcohol as the solvent and added equivalent amounts of sodium iodide when alkyl chlorides or bromides were the starting materials. The quaternary salt which separated from the reaction mixture was hydrolyzed directly with hydrogen chloride gas.

Methyl alcohol was employed in the reaction with some dihalides.[3] Only one halogen atom was replaced. For example, 3-bromopropylamine was prepared from 1,3-dibromopropane. Another procedure, which involves isolation of the hexamethylenetetramine quaternary salt, has been described.[4] The salt is heated in an excess of concentrated hydrochloric acid, and the formaldehyde which is formed is removed by steam distillation.

β-Alanine[5] has been prepared from β-bromopropionic acid via the Delépine reaction.

References

1. M. Delépine, *Bull. soc. chim. Paris* **13**, 355 (1895); **17**, 290 (1897); *Compt. rend. acad. sci.* **120**, 501 (1895); **124**, 292 (1897).
2. A. Galat and G. Elion, *J. Am. Chem. Soc.* **61**, 3585 (1939).
3. L. H. Amundsen and A. M. Pulito, paper read at the 118th meeting of the American Chemical Society, Chicago, 1950.
4. J. Graymore and D. R. Davies, *J. Chem. Soc.* p. 293 (1945).
5. N. L. Wender, *J. Am. Chem. Soc.* **71**, 375 (1949).

Dieckmann Reaction

Walter Dieckmann (1869–1925) was born in Hamburg, Germany, the son of a merchant. He studied chemistry at Heidelberg, then at the Technical Institute at Charlottenburg, and finally in Munich under E. Bamberger. He obtained the Ph.D. degree in 1892 after working on tetrahydroisoquinolines. After serving as an assistant to von Baeyer in his private laboratory, Dieckmann returned to Munich, where, in 1898, he joined the faculty. He died while working in the chemical laboratory of the Bavarian Academy of Sciences.

Dieckmann's cyclization procedure for the formation of cyclic β-keto esters has been used in many fields of organic chemistry. He published many papers on acetoacetic ester condensations and desmotropic problems.

The Dieckmann reaction consists in the intramolecular condensation of esters of dibasic acids in the presence of a base to give a cyclic β-keto ester.[1] A typical example of the Dieckmann reaction is the

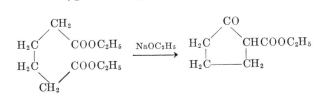

formation of ethyl 2-oxocyclopentanecarboxylate from ethyl adipate. Sodium hydride has been shown to be a very good condensing agent for this condensation.[2] The β-keto ester may be hydrolyzed and decarboxylated to give a cyclic ketone.

This cyclization reaction is a special type of *Claisen condensation,* and has a similar mechanism. An isotopic effect study of the mechanism has shown that the rate-determining step is the formation of a carbon-carbon bond, the reaction of the enolate with the carbonyl group.[3]

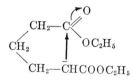

The effect of alkyl groups on the Dieckmann cyclization has been investigated by Chakravarti.[4] Where two possible isomers can be formed, steric hindrance due to alkyl groups appears to be involved in lessening the activity of a methylene group. For example, with ethyl β,β-dimethyladipate, only one product, ethyl 4,4-dimethyl-2-oxo-cyclopentanecarboxylate was obtained.

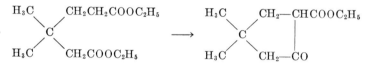

Both alicyclic and heterocyclic keto esters have been prepared via the Dieckmann reaction. An example in which nitrogen is the hetero atom[5] is the formation of ethyl 1-methyl-3-oxoisonipecotate (II) from the diester (I).

$$CH_3-N\Big\langle{CH_2CH_2CH_2COOC_2H_5 \atop CH_2COOC_2H_5} \longrightarrow CH_3-N\Big\langle{CH_2-CH_2 \atop CH_2-CO}\Big\rangle CHCOOC_2H_5$$

I   II

A variety of tetrahydrothiophenes have been prepared by the Dieckmann method.[6] Starting with (III), two isomeric cyclic β-keto esters (IV and V) may be obtained. When the reaction was carried out at 80° the main product was the keto ester (IV); with ether as the solvent, methyl 3-oxo-tetrahydro-2-thiophenecarboxylate (V) predominated.

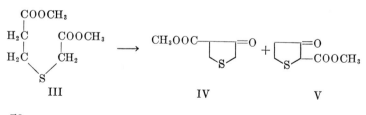

III   IV   V

References

1. W. Dieckmann, *Ber. deut. Chem. Ges.* **27**, 102, 965 (1894); *Ber. deut. Chem. Ges.* **33**, 2670 (1900).
2. D. K. Banerjee and P. R. Shafer, *J. Am. Chem. Soc.* **72**, 1931 (1950); W. S. Johnson, A. R. Jones, and W. P. Schneider, *J. Chem. Soc.* **72**, 2395 (1950).
3. W. J. Carrick and A. Fry, *J. Am. Chem. Soc.* **77**, 4381 (1955).
4. R. N. Chakravarti, *J. Chem. Soc.* p. 1028 (1947).
5. E. A. Prill and S. M. McElvain, *J. Am. Chem. Soc.* **55**, 1233 (1933).
6. See D. E. Wolf and K. Folkers, *in* "Organic Reactions" (R. Adams, ed.), Vol. VI, pp. 449–463. Wiley, New York, 1951.

Diels-Alder Reaction

Otto Diels (1876–1954) was born in Hamburg, Germany. He received his doctor's degree in 1899 at Berlin and became an assistant to Emil Fischer. He taught at Berlin, where he rose to the rank of associate professor in 1914. Two years later, Diels joined the faculty at Kiel, where he became head of the chemistry department.

One of Diel's main interests was sterol chemistry. He showed that sterols could be dehydrogenated to form the hydrocarbon $C_{18}H_{16}$. He worked on the structure of and synthesized cantharidin. In 1906, Diels discovered carbon suboxide and in 1927, with his student, Kurt Alder, began the work on the diene syntheses. For their far-reaching contributions in the field of organic syntheses, Diels and Alder were awarded the Nobel Prize for chemistry in 1950.

* * *

Kurt Alder (1902–1958) was born in Königshütte, Upper Silesia. He studied at Berlin, and then under Otto Diels at Kiel, where he received his Ph.D. degree in 1926. He joined the faculty there and in 1934 was appointed professor of chemistry. Then he served as a research director for several years at the Bayer dye works, and in 1940 went to the University of Cologne to head the chemical institute. In 1951, he received a call to assume the chair in chemistry at the University of Marburg.

Alder is probably best known for his work with Diels on the diene synthesis. For this work they shared the Nobel Prize for chemistry in 1950. Alder's interests also included problems of stereochemistry, autoxidation, and polymerization.

In 1928 Diels and Alder[1] found that butadiene reacts vigorously with maleic anhydride to give a quantitative yield of a six-membered ring, *cis*-1,2,3,6-tetrahydrophthalic anhydride.

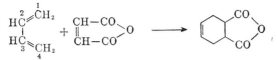

The condensation involves a 1,4 addition of the ethylenic group to the diene with the formation of a double bond in the 2,3 position.

This reaction of a conjugated diene with a compound having an ethylenic or acetylenic bond usually activated by some group such as CO, COOH, CN, NO_2 is a general one and has a wide scope.[2] A large variety of compounds containing an activated double or triple bond (called dienophiles) and dienes have been employed in this reaction. With an acetylenic dienophile such as acetylenedicarboxylic acid, the reaction with butadiene gives 3,6-dihydrophthalic acid.

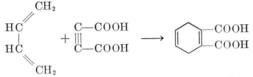

The reaction is also useful in explaining many polymerizations involving unsaturated compounds, since a diene can also behave as a dienophile.

In many instances the reaction is carried out by mixing the diene and the dienophile in equimolecular proportions at room temperature. An inert solvent such as benzene or ether may be added to moderate the reaction. With less reactive dienophiles the reaction conditions are more vigorous. The yields obtained in the Diels-Alder reaction are usually good.

By carrying out the reaction in nitrobenzene solution, dehydrogenation of the hydroaromatic product may occur to give an aromatic compounds. In these cases no reversible reaction is possible. For example, 1,4-diphenylbutadiene reacts with 1,4-naphthoquinone in hot nitrobenzene to give a 70% yield of 1,4-diphenylanthraquinone.[3]

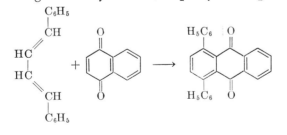

Unusual bridge-ring compounds have been synthesized via the Diels-Alder reaction. An illustration is the addition of 2,3-dihydro-thiophene 1-dioxide to cyclopentadiene.[4]

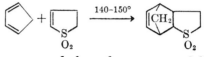

Tertiary nitro compounds have been prepared by the reaction of 2-nitropropene and 2-nitro-2-butene with cyclopentadiene.[5]

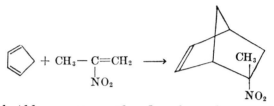

The Diels-Alder reaction with *o*-fluorobromobenzene and lithium-amalgam in the presence of furan is described by Wittig.[6] A dehydro-benzene (benzyne) is pictured as the dienophile.

Woodward and Katz[7] have recently proposed an unsymmetrical mechanism for the Diels-Alder reaction involving a two-stage process in which the two bonds linking the diene to dienophile are formed separately. The one-step mechanism has received support by Dewar.[8]

References

1. O. Diels and K. Alder, *Ann. Chem. Liebigs* **460**, 98 (1928).
2. For reviews of the Diels-Alder reaction, see M. C. Kloetzel, *in* "Organic Reactions" (R. Adams, ed.), Vol. IV, p. 1. Wiley, New York, 1948; H. L. Holmes, *in* "Organic Reactions" (R. Adams, ed.), Vol. IV, p. 60. Wiley, New York, 1948; L. W. Butz and A. W. Rytina, *in* "Organic Reactions" (R. Adams, ed.), Vol. V, p. 136. Wiley, New York, 1949.
3. E. Bergmann, L. Haskelberg, and F. Bergmann, *J. Org. Chem.* **7**, 303 (1942).
4. K. Alder, H. F. Rickert, and E. Windemuth, *Ber. deut. Chem. Ges.* **71**, 2451 (1938).
5. W. E. Noland and R. E. Bambury, *J. Am. Chem. Soc.* **77**, 6386 (1957).
6. G. Wittig, *Angew. Chem.* **69**, 245 (1957).
7. R. B. Woodward and T. J. Katz, *Tetrahedron* **5**, 70 (1959).
8. M. J. S. Dewar, *Tetrahedron Letters No. 4*, 16 (1959); see also R. B. Woodward and T. J. Katz, *Tetrahedron Letters No. 5*, 19 (1959).

Doebner Synthesis

Oskar Gustav Doebner (1850–1907) was born in Meiningen, Thüringen, Germany. He studied botany at Jena and later at Munich, where he also studied under Liebig. After active service in the Franco-Prussian War, he resumed his studies at Leipzig, where he attended Kolbe's lectures. Doebner received his doctorate at Tübingen (1873) under Fittig. He served as an assistant to Otto at Braunschweig (1874–1875) and later to Hofmann at Berlin. From 1899 he taught at the University of Halle. Doebner is known for his quinoline syntheses.

The preparation of cinchoninic acids by the condensation of an arylamine, an aliphatic or aromatic aldehyde, and pyruvic acids is known as the Doebner synthesis.[1] A typical example is the formation of 2-phenylcinchoninic acid (cinchophen), which may be illustrated in the following manner.

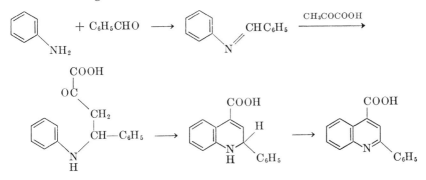

In connection with the preparation of some antimalarial drugs, Lutz and co-workers[2] have studied the conditions for optimum yields in the Doebner synthesis. One of the prerequisites is the use of freshly distilled pyruvic acid. Although the yields of cinchoninic acids are

81

usually not high, the method is a useful one because of the accessibility of starting materials.

The formation of a dihydroquinoline in the above illustration is similar to the intermediates proposed for the Skraup (p. 218) and Doebner-Miller (p. 83) reactions. A disproportionation, or, more likely, an oxidation by the intermediate Schiff base, benzylideneaniline, converts the dihydro compound to the cinchoninic acid.

References

1. O. Doebner, *Ann. Chem. Liebigs* **242**, 265 (1887).
2. R. E. Lutz, *et al., J. Am. Chem. Soc.* **68**, 1813 (1946); see also R. C. Elderfield, ed., *in* "Heterocyclic Compounds," Vol. 4, pp. 25–29. Wiley, New York, 1952.

Doebner-Miller Synthesis

The formation of quinoline derivatives by heating an arylamine with an aldehyde or a mixture of aldehydes in concentrated hydrochloric or sulfuric acid is called the Doebner-Miller synthesis.[1] The aldehyde probably undergoes self-condensation to give an α,β-unsaturated aldehyde which then reacts with the amine. The reaction is similar to the Skraup reaction and is believed to proceed through a dihydroquinoline which is later oxidized to the quinaldine derivative.[2]

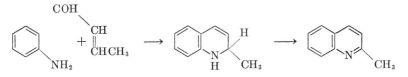

The yields in the Doebner-Miller synthesis have been markedly improved by a modified procedure involving the use of m-nitrobenzenesulfonic acid as a water-soluble oxidizing agent and 60–70% sulfuric acid.[3] The formation of 5- and 7-chloroquinaldines from m-chloroaniline and paraldehyde by this modified procedure was investigated by Spivey and Curd,[4] who showed that the proportion of the 7-substituted isomer increased with a decrease in acid concentration.

References

1. O. Doebner and W. von Miller, *Ber. deut. Chem. Ges.* **16**, 2464 (1883).
2. See R. C. Elderfield, ed., in "Heterocyclic Compounds," Vol. 4, pp. 10–17. Wiley, New York, 1952.
3. German Patent 567,273; and W. P. Utermohlen, *J. Org. Chem.* **8**, 544 (1943).
4. A. M. Spivey and F. H. S. Curd, *J. Chem. Soc.* p. 2656 (1949).

Duff Reaction

James Cooper Duff (1888–   ) was born in Glasgow, Scotland. He received the M.Sc. degree from the University of Manchester and the D.Sc. degree in 1923 from the College of Technology, Birmingham, for independent research in organic chemistry. At present, Professor Duff is head of the department of chemistry at the College of Technology, Birmingham. His interests in chemistry include an investigation of complex metal amines and the reaction of phenolic compounds with hexamethylenetetramine.

The formation of o-hydroxybenzaldehydes from phenols and hexamethylenetetramine is called the Duff reaction.[1]

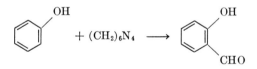

The method, which is a general one, is quicker and usually gives purer products than the Reimer-Tiemann reaction.[2]

When the reaction was carried out by heating the reactants at 150–160° with glyceroboric acid in anhydrous glycerin and then treating the mixture with dilute sulfuric acid, no intermediate products were obtained. However, if the phenol, hexamethylenetetramine, and boric acid were heated in 2-ethoxyethanol, a secondary amine (I) could be isolated.[3]

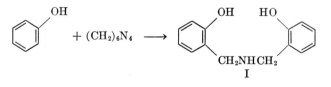

I

Heating the secondary amine with hexamethylenetetramine in acetic acid resulted in dehydrogenation to give the Schiff base (II). The latter was then hydrolyzed to the phenolic aldehyde (III).

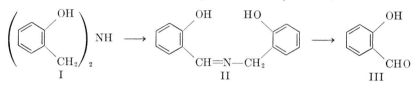

I   II   III

References

1. J. C. Duff and E. J. Bills, *J. Chem. Soc.* p. 1987 (1932); J. C. Duff, *J. Chem. Soc.* p. 547 (1941).
2. L. N. Ferguson, *Chem. Revs.* 38, 230 (1946).
3. J. C. Duff and V. I. Furness, *J. Chem. Soc.* p. 1512 (1951).

Elbs Reaction

Karl Elbs (1858–1933) was born in Alt-Breisach, Germany. He received the Ph.D. degree in 1880 from the University of Freiburg and was appointed professor of chemistry there seven years later. In 1894, Elbs was chosen to teach physical chemistry at the University of Giessen, where he later became professor of experimental chemistry.

Elbs' book (1891) on the synthetic methods of preparation of carbon compounds was the forerunner of the works of Lassar-Cohn and Houben-Weyl. In 1902, he wrote a book dealing with electrochemical preparations. His work on the electrochemical reduction and oxidation of organic compounds, especially on the reduction of aromatic nitro compounds, is valuable from both a scientific and a practical viewpoint. Elbs investigated the preparation of persulfuric acid and its salts, which he used for oxidations. He also found that a mixture of sodium persulfate and iodine is an excellent medium for iodination of organic compounds.

The cyclization by pyrolysis of diaryl ketones having a methyl or methylene substituent *ortho* to the carbonyl group is termed the Elbs reaction.[1] An example is the preparation of 2-methylanthracene from 2,5-dimethylbenzophenone.[2]

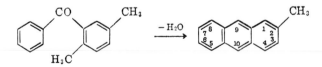

The reaction is usually carried out by heating the ketone derivative at the critical pyrolysis temperature[3] (around 400°) until water is no longer eliminated. In many instances, side reactions which occur during pyrolysis make difficult the isolation and purification of the desired product. Although the yields in the Elbs reaction are usually low, the method is useful in preparing polycyclic aromatic hydrocarbons otherwise difficult to obtain. Many of these compounds have been found to possess carcinogenic activity.

The mechanism of the Elbs reaction has not been definitely established. A dihydroanthranol (I) has been suggested[4,5] as a pos-

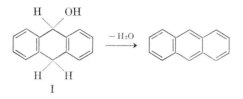

I

sible intermediate in the reaction. It was shown,[6] using deuterium as a tracer, that the nuclear-displaced hydrogen appeared at the 9 position in the anthracene molecule.

References

1. A review of the Elbs reaction is given by L. F. Fieser, *in* "Organic Reactions" (R. Adams, ed.), Vol. I, p. 129. Wiley, New York, 1942.
2. K. Elbs and E. Larsen, *Ber. deut. Chem. Ges.* **17**, 2847 (1884); K. Elbs, *J. prakt. Chem.* **41**, 1 (1890).
3. L. F. Fieser and A. M. Seligman, *J. Am. Chem. Soc.* **58**, 2482 (1936).
4. L. F. Fieser and E. M. Dietz, *Ber. deut. Chem. Ges.* **62**, 1827 (1929).
5. J. W. Cook, *J. Chem. Soc.* p. 487 (1931).
6. C. D. Hurd and J. Azorlosa, *J. Am. Chem. Soc.* **73**, 37 (1951).

Elbs Persulfate Oxidation

The oxidation of phenols to dihydric phenols by means of potassium persulfate in alkaline solution is commonly called the Elbs persulfate oxidation.[1] The reaction is usually carried out by adding an aqueous solution of potassium persulfate to a cooled solution of the phenol in dilute caustic followed by acidification. Oxidation takes place in the *para* position unless it is occupied, in which case some oxidation occurs in the *ortho* position.[2]

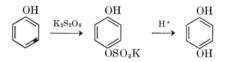

The Elbs oxidation[3] has been applied with substituted phenols, naphthols, coumarins, flavones, and N-heterocyclic compounds. The yields are often low but the products are usually obtained in a pure state. An example of the reaction in the coumarin series[4] is the preparation of 5,7-dimethoxy-6-hydroxycoumarin (II) from the dimethoxy compound (I).

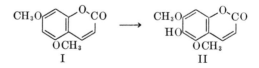

The reaction has been recently applied to 2- and 3-hydroxypyridines.[5] In both cases the main product isolated after hydrolysis of the sulfate esters is 2,5-dihydroxypyridine.

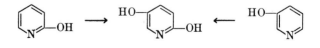

References

1. K. Elbs, *J. prakt. Chem.* **48**, 179 (1893).
2. W. Baker and N. C. Brown, *J. Chem. Soc.* p. 2303 (1948).
3. A review of the Elbs persulfate oxidation is given by S. M. Sethna, *Chem. Revs.* **49**, 91 (1951).
4. V. J. Dalvi, R. B. Desai, and S. Sethna, *J. Indian Chem. Soc.* **28**, 366 (1951).
5. E. J. Behrman and B. M. Pitt, *J. Am. Chem. Soc.* **80**, 3717 (1958).

Emde Degradation

Hermann Emde (1880–1935) was born in Opladen, Germany, the son of a chemist. He studied chemistry, pharmacy, and nutrition at the Technical Institute at Braunschweig, and at the University of Marburg, where he obtained the doctor's degree. He joined the faculty at Braunschweig and then worked under Thiele at Strassburg. In 1928, Emde was appointed assistant professor at Basel and three years later left for Königsberg, where he became director of the Pharmaceutical Chemical Institute. He devoted much of his time to the investigation of natural products and the cleavage of quaternary ammonium salts.

When an aqueous or alcoholic solution of a quaternary ammonium halide is treated with sodium amalgam, a carbon-nitrogen bond is ruptured. This method of degradation, known as the Emde degradation,[1] has served as a useful tool in the determination of structures of some alkaloids and other nitrogen compounds.[2]

Emde showed that when N,N-dimethyltetrahydroquinolinium chloride (I) was treated with sodium amalgam, o-propyldimethylaniline was formed.

With the quaternary compound (I), no ring opening is obtained by the Hofmann degradation; methyl alcohol is split out, and N-methyltetrahydroquinoline is formed.

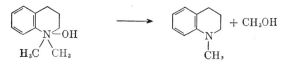

With tetrahydroisoquinolinium halides, the same product, *o*-vinyl benzyldimethylamine (II), is obtained by either the Hofmann or the Emde degradation.

However, the quaternary salt from the amine (II) can be further degraded by the Emde process to give *o*-methylstyrene (III).

A modified Emde degradation using Raney nickel alloy in place of sodium amalgam has been reported.[3] By this procedure, reductive fission of quaternary ammonium salts may be effected in good yield under mild conditions and in a short time.

References

1. H. Emde, *Ann. Chem. Liebigs* **391,** 88 (1912).
2. H. Emde and H. Kull, *Arch. Pharm.* **272,** 469 (1934).
3. S. Sugasawa and S. Ushioda, *Tetrahedron* **5,** 48 (1959).

Erlenmeyer-Plöchl Azlactone Synthesis

Emil Erlenmeyer, Jr. (1864–1921) was born in Heidelberg, Germany. His father, Emil Erlenmeyer (1825–1909), one of the leaders in the development of organic chemistry, was professor of chemistry at the University of Heidelberg. The son was undoubtedly influenced by his esteemed father, and it is not surprising that his life's work was in a similar field.

Erlenmeyer studied science at Heidelberg and chemistry at Bonn under Kekulé. He continued his studies at Marburg and Darmstadt, and then at Göttingen where he received his doctorate in 1888. He joined the faculty at Bonn in 1891, and five years later became professor of chemistry at Strassburg.

Wishing to be independent, Erlenmeyer started a private teaching laboratory (1901) where many graduate students joined him.

In 1907, he was called to the Imperial Biological Institute at Dahlem where he was able to carry out his scientific investigations particularly in the field of cinnamic acid derivatives and on problems dealing with plant physiology.

The condensation of an aldehyde with an acyl derivative (usually benzoyl or acetyl) of glycine in the presence of acetic anhydride and sodium acetate to give an oxazolone (azlactone) is commonly referred to as the Erlenmeyer-Plöchl azlactone synthesis.[1-3] With benzaldehyde and acetylglycine the product is 4-benzylidene-2-methyl-5-oxazolone.[4]

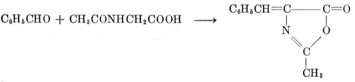

$$C_6H_5CHO + CH_3CONHCH_2COOH \longrightarrow$$

The reaction is a special type of Perkin reaction and is best suited for aromatic aldehydes. However, lower aliphatic aldehydes have been shown to react with 2-phenyl-5-oxazolone to give the unsaturated azlactones.[5]

Bennett and Niemann[6] demonstrated that in several instances a transacylation reaction occurred during the azlactone synthesis which

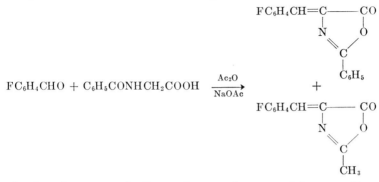

$$FC_6H_4CHO + C_6H_5CONHCH_2COOH \xrightarrow[NaOAc]{Ac_2O}$$

involved replacement of a benzoyl group by an acetyl group. For example, in the condensation of p-fluorobenzaldehyde with hippuric acid in the presence of acetic anhydride and sodium acetate, the product consisted of a mixture of 2-phenyl- and 2-methyl-4-(p-fluorobenzylidene)-5-oxazolone.

The azlactones are useful intermediates for the syntheses of a variety of different types of compounds including α-amino and α-keto acids. Hydrolysis of the azlactones yields α-acylaminoacrylic acids which on reduction give α-amino acids.

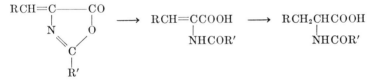

Phenylalanine has been prepared by this method in 86% yield.[7]

Treatment of the azlactone with amines and amino acids produces amides and dipeptide derivatives. Hydrolysis with strong mineral acids or alkalies leads to α-keto acids. 3,4-Dimethoxyphenylacetic acid has been prepared in this manner by oxidation of the α-keto acid with hydrogen peroxide.[8]

RCH=C ——CO
| |
N   O
 \\   /
   C
   |
   R′
$\xrightarrow{OH^-}$ RCH₂COCOOH $\xrightarrow{H_2O_2}$ RCH₂COOH

Arylacetonitriles may be prepared from the α-keto acids via the oximes.[9]

$$\text{RCH}_2\text{COCOOH} \longrightarrow \underset{\underset{\text{NOH}}{\|}}{\text{RCH}_2\text{CCOOH}} \overset{\text{Ac}_2\text{O}}{\longrightarrow} \text{RCH}_2\text{CN}$$

References

1. J. Plöchl, *Ber. deut. Chem. Ges.* **17**, 1616 (1884); E. Erlenmeyer, *Ann. Chem. Liebigs* **275**, 1 (1893).
2. A review of the snythesis is given by H. E. Carter, *in* "Organic Reactions" (R. Adams, ed.), Vol. III, p. 198. Wiley, New York, 1946.
3. The chemistry of 5-oxazolones is reviewed by E. Baltazzi, *Quart. Revs.* (*London*) **9**, 150 (1955).
4. R. M. Herbst and D. Shemin, *in* "Organic Syntheses" (A. H. Blatt, ed.), Coll. Vol. II, p. 1. Wiley, New York, 1943.
5. M. Crawford and W. T. Little, *J. Chem. Soc.* p. 729 (1959).
6. E. L. Bennett and C. Niemann, *J. Am. Chem. Soc.* **72**, 1803 (1950).
7. R. M. Herbst and D. Shemin, *in* "Organic Syntheses" (A. H. Blatt, ed.), Coll. Vol. II, p. 491. Wiley, New York, 1943.
8. H. R. Snyder, J. S. Buck, and W. S. Ide, *in* "Organic Syntheses" (A. H. Blatt, ed.), Coll. Vol. II, p. 333. Wiley, New York, 1943.
9. J. S. Buck, R. Baltzly, and W. S. Ide, *J. Am. Chem. Soc.* **60**, 1789 (1938).

Faworskii Rearrangement

Aleksei J. Faworskiï (1860–1945) was born in Selo Pavlova, Russia. He studied at the University of St. Petersburg, where he received the Ph.D. degree in 1896 and a year later became professor of technical chemistry and technology. In 1902, Faworskiï was appointed professor of chemistry at the University of St. Petersburg.

The rearrangement of α-halo ketones in the presence of a basic catalyst to give acids or esters is referred to as the Faworskiï rearrangement.[1,2] For example, 2-chlorocyclohexanone, on treatment with potassium alcoholate, gives cyclopentanecarboxylic acid.

With C^{14}-labeled 2-chlorocyclohexanone, Loftfield[3] has shown that isotopic distribution of the product favors a cyclopropanone intermediate.[4]

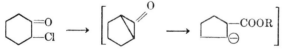

Sodium benzyl oxide was found to give the best yield in the above rearrangement.[5]

Stork and Borowitz[5] have also shown that the *cis* and *trans* isomers of 1-acetyl-1-chloro-2-methylcyclohexane rearrange to 1,2-dimethyl-cyclohexanecarboxylic acid with inversion of stereochemistry at the carbon bearing the halogen atom.

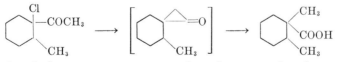

In the aliphatic series, a variety of products may be obtained depending upon the reaction conditions. The rearrangement of the α-

chloro ketone (I) with sodium ethoxide gives the ester (II). With sodium methoxide in methanol, the hydroxyacetal (III) is formed; sodium methoxide in ether suspension gives the ester (II), R = CH₃.

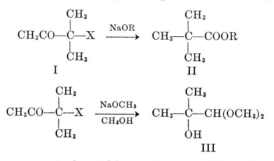

The rearrangement of α,α'-dibromo ketones with sodium methoxide gives α,β-unsaturated esters.[6]

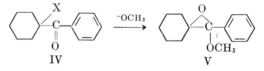

Under the same conditions α,β-dibromo ketones give β,γ-unsaturated esters.

$$R—CH—C(CH_3)COCH_3 \longrightarrow RCH=C(CH_3)CH_2COOCH_3$$
$$\underset{Br}{|} \quad \underset{Br}{|}$$

Stevens and Farkas have shown that the epoxy ether (V) from α-halocyclohexyl phenyl ketone (IV) is not an intermediate in the rearrangement of IV to the acid (VI).[7]

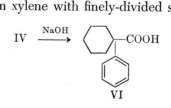

The formation of VI from the halo ketone (IV) is effected in 53% yield by refluxing in xylene with finely-divided sodium hydroxide.[8]

IV $\xrightarrow{\text{NaOH}}$ ⬡—COOH
                          |
                          C₆H₅

VI

References

1. A. E. Faworskiĭ, *J. prakt. Chem.* **88**, 658 (1913).
2. A review of the Faworskiĭ rearrangement is given by R. Jacquier, *Bull. soc. chim. France* pp. D35–45 (1950).
3. R. B. Loftsfield, *J. Am. Chem. Soc.* **73**, 4707 (1951).
4. See also, J. G. Burr and M. J. S. Dewar, *J. Chem. Soc.* p. 1201 (1954).
5. G. Stork and I. J. Borowitz, *J. Am. Chem. Soc.* **82**, 4307 (1960).
6. R. B. Wagner and J. A. Moore, *J. Am. Chem. Soc.* **72**, 974 (1950).
7. C. L. Stevens and E. Farkas, *J. Am. Chem. Soc.* **74**, 618 (1952).
8. C. L. Stevens and E. Farkas, *J. Am. Chem. Soc.* **74**, 5352 (1952).

Fischer Indole Synthesis

Emil Fischer (1852–1919) was born in Euskirchen, near Bonn, Germany. He studied at Bonn and then at Strassburg under von Baeyer. When von Baeyer succeeded Liebig at Munich in 1875, Fischer accompanied him as an assistant. He taught at the Universities of Erlangen and Würzburg and then succeeded Hofmann as professor of chemistry at Berlin, where his fame as an organic chemist attracted students from all over the world.

Among the numerous outstanding achievements of Fischer are the discovery of phenylhydrazine (1875) and the synthesis of uric acid (1897), polypeptides, and tannins. For his brilliant work on the structure and syntheses of sugars and purines, Fischer was awarded the Nobel Prize for chemistry in 1902.

The preparation of indoles by heating a phenylhydrazone of an aldehyde or ketone in the presence of a catalyst such as zinc chloride, dilute sulfuric acid, glacial acetic acid, or alcoholic hydrogen chloride is known as the Fischer indole synthesis.[1] This general reaction[2] involves an intramolecular condensation with elimination of ammonia.

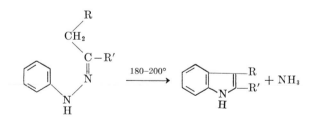

Using N^{15} as a tracer element, Allen and Wilson[3] demonstrated that the N^{15} in the *alpha* position of the phenylhydrazone is retained in the indole nucleus. This was confirmed in a later investigation.[4] The N^{15} in the *beta* position of the hydrazone is eliminated as ammonia.

The generally accepted mechanism of the Fischer indole synthesis may be represented as follows:

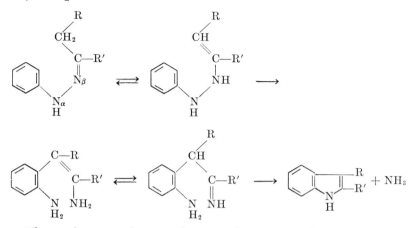

The cyclization of some electron-releasing *m*-substituted phenyl-hydrazones has been shown to give a preponderance of 6- over 4-substituted indoles.[5] The reverse is usually true of *meta*-directing groups.

3-Indoleacetic acid has been prepared by the Fischer ring closure of succinaldehydic acid phenylhydrazone.[6] The condensation of N-benzyl-N-(*p*-methoxyphenyl)hydrazine hydrochloride with 5-phthali-mido-2-pentanone in glacial acetic acid proceeds smoothly to give the expected indole.[7] Treatment with hydrazine yields 1-benzyl-2-methyl-5-methoxytryptamine.

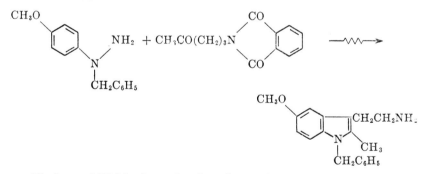

Blades and Wilds[8] have developed a method for the preparation of substituted indoles in good yields from the reaction of diazo ketones

99

with aniline salts and aniline. For example, from the diazo ketone derived from diazomethane and 4-chlorobenzoyl chloride, 2-(4-chlorophenyl)-indole was obtained in 80% yield.

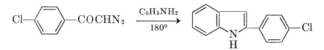

Carlin[9] has investigated the Fischer indole synthesis with 2,6-disubstituted phenylhydrazones. A non-aromatic intermediate of structure I has been postulated to account for the products obtained.

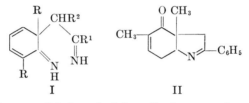

With acetophenone 2,6-dimethylphenylhydrazone the major product isolated was 2-phenyl-3a,5-dimethyl-3a,4,7,7a-tetrahydro [3H] pseudoindolone-4 (II).

References

1. E. Fischer and F. Jourdan, *Ber. deut. Chem. Ges.* **16,** 2241 (1883).
2. A review of the reaction is given by R. B. Van Order and H. G. Lindwall, *Chem. Revs.* **30,** 78 (1942); see, also, P. L. Julian, E. W. Meyer, and H. C. Printy, *in* "Heterocyclic Compounds" (R. C. Elderfield, ed.), Vol. 3, pp. 8–16. Wiley, New York, 1952.
3. C. F. H. Allen and C. V. Wilson, *J. Am. Chem. Soc.* **65,** 611 (1943); see also for previous references on the mechanism.
4. K. Clusius and H. R. Weisser, *Helv. Chim. Acta* **35,** 400 (1952).
5. D. W. Ockenden and K. Schofield, *J. Chem. Soc.* p. 3175 (1957).
6. S. W. Fox and M. W. Bullock, *J. Am. Chem. Soc.* **73,** 2754, 2756 (1951).
7. M. Sletzinger, W. A. Gaines, and W. V. Ruyle, *Chem. & Ind.* (*London*) p. 1215 (1957).
8. C. E. Blades and A. L. Wilds, *J. Org. Chem.* **21,** 1013 (1956).
9. R. B. Carlin and D. P. Carlson, *J. Am. Chem. Soc.* **81,** 4673 (1959).

Friedel-Crafts Reaction

Charles Friedel (1832–1899) was born in Strasbourg, France. He studied chemistry at the Sorbonne under Wurtz and received his doctor's degree in 1869. He also studied mineralogy at the École des Mines, where he was appointed curator. In 1876, Friedel became professor of mineralogy at the Sorbonne, and eight years later he succeeded Wurtz in the professorial chair of organic chemistry.

Friedel made many outstanding contributions in mineralogy and organic chemistry. He synthesized isopropyl alcohol, lactic acid, and glycerin, and showed the similarity of silicon and carbon compounds. He worked with Crafts on the preparation of esters of silicic acid, and the action of aluminum chloride in the synthesis of alkyl and acyl aromatic derivatives.

Friedel received many honors, including the Davy Medal in 1880, and honorary membership in many foreign societies. He was one of the founders of the French Chemical Society and served as its president four times.

* * *

James Mason Crafts (1839–1917) was born in Boston, Massachusetts. He received the B.S. degree from the Lawrence Scientific School, studied engineering at Cambridge for one year, and then went to Freiburg (1859) to study mineralogy. A year later he studied under Bunsen at Heidelberg and then went to Paris (1861) to study under Wurtz. In 1865, Crafts returned to the United States. The following year he became the dean of the chemical faculty at the newly founded Cornell University. After four years there he assumed the chair of general chemistry at the Massachusetts Institute of Technology. From 1874 until 1891, Crafts was at the École des Mines in Paris, where he collaborated with Professor Friedel on the important Friedel-Crafts reaction. Crafts also made important contributions in thermometry. He returned to his teaching position at the Massachusetts Institute of Technology in 1891, and later became president of the Institute.

The Friedel-Crafts reaction includes the alkylation[1] and acylation[2] of aromatic compounds by means of an alkyl or acyl halide in the presence of aluminum chloride.[3] The reaction is illustrated by the following examples:

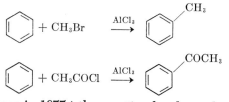

Since its discovery in 1877,[4] the reaction has been the subject of considerable investigation. A wide variety of aromatic compounds (benzene, substituted benzenes, naphthalenes, heterocycles, etc.) have been alkylated and acylated by this method.

Many different alkylating agents (alkyl halides, olefins, alcohols, esters) and catalysts ($AlCl_3$, $AlBr_3$, H_2SO_4, BF_3, HF, H_3PO_4, P_2O_5, $ZnCl_2$, $SnCl_4$) have been used in the Friedel-Crafts reaction.

Depending to a large extent upon the ratio of the reactants, one or more alkyl groups may be introduced into the aromatic nucleus. In many instances a mixture of products is obtained. For example, the reaction of benzene with an excess of ethyl chloride in the presence of aluminum chloride gives a mixture of tetraethylbenzene, pentaethylbenzene, and hexaethylbenzene.

In the case of the acylation reaction (with acids, acid halides, and acid anhydrides) only one acyl group is introduced into the aromatic compound. Like other deactivating groups (NO_2, COOH) the acyl group has a detrimental effect on the Friedel-Crafts reaction. The formation of acetophenone from benzene and acetyl chloride, and benzoylpropionic acid from benzene and succinic anhydride are examples of the acylation reaction.

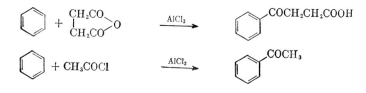

The mechanism of the Friedel-Crafts reaction is generally believed to involve the formation of an alkyl or acyl carbonium ion, followed by reaction with the aromatic nucleus.

$$RCl + AlCl_3 \rightleftharpoons R^+ + (AlCl_4)^-$$

$$RCOCl + AlCl_3 \rightleftharpoons R\overset{+}{C}O + (AlCl_4)^-$$

Brown and Pearsall[5] suggested that complexes formed from the aromatic hydrocarbon, aluminum halide, and hydrogen halide play an important part in the Friedel-Crafts reaction by serving as a polar medium which facilitates solution of the aluminum halide and formation of ionic intermediates.

Polyphosphoric acid has proved to be an effective catalyst in Friedel-Crafts reactions, especially in those reactions requiring milder conditions. Phenolic ethers are not cleaved with this condensing agent.[6]

References

1. For reviews of alkylations by the Friedel-Crafts reaction, see C. C. Price, *in* "Organic Reactions" (R. Adams, ed.), Vol. III, p. 1. Wiley, New York, 1946; K. L. Nelson, *Ind. Eng. Chem.* 48, 1670 (1956).
2. For reviews of acylations by the Friedel-Crafts reaction, see W. S. Johnson, *in* "Organic Reactions" (R. Adams, ed.), Vol. II, p. 130. Wiley, New York, 1944; E. Berliner, *in* "Organic Reactions" (R. Adams, ed.), Vol. V, p. 229. Wiley, New York, 1949; K. L. Nelson, *Ind. Eng. Chem.* 48, 1670 (1956).
3. See C. A. Thomas, "Anhydrous Aluminum Chloride in Organic Chemistry." American Chemical Society Monograph No. 87, Reinhold, New York, 1941.
4. C. Friedel and J. M. Crafts, *Compt. rend. acad. sci.* 84, 1292, 1450 (1877).
5. H. C. Brown and H. W. Pearsall, *J. Am. Chem. Soc.* 74, 191 (1952).
6. P. D. Gardner, *J. Am. Chem. Soc.* 76, 4550 (1954); a review of the use of polyphosphoric acid as a reagent in organic chemistry is given by F. Uhlig and H. R. Snyder, *in* "Advances in Organic Chemistry" (R. A. Raphael, E. C. Taylor, and H. Wynberg, (eds.), Vol. I, pp. 35–81. Interscience, New York, 1960.

103

Friedländer Synthesis

Paul Friedländer (1857–1923) was born in Königsberg, Germany. At the University there he studied under Graebe and then at Munich under von Baeyer. In 1883, he became an assistant professor at Munich and after one year left to direct a small dyestuff factory in Offenbach. In 1888, Friedländer returned to academic life at Karlsruhe and from 1895 to 1911 served as professor of chemistry at Vienna.

Having worked with von Baeyer, Friedländer was interested in the structure and synthesis of indigo. He carried out fundamental research on isatin derivatives, transforming chloroisatin into indigo. He showed that phenanthraquinone was transformed by alkali into diphenyleneglycolic acid, and with von Baeyer described indoxyl for the first time. In 1888, Friedländer began his collection of patent literature, a work which is valuable source material for the organic chemist.

Friedländer's love for travel brought him to many lands, including America, Canada, and Cuba. On some of his travels he was accompanied by Emil Fischer and Victor Meyer. Friedländer was also interested in music and was an accomplished pianist. On one occasion he played at the home of F. Haber before Einstein.

The condensation of o-aminobenzaldehydes with compounds having the structure —CH_2CO— to yield quinoline derivatives is known as the Friedländer synthesis.[1] This general reaction is usually carried out by refluxing an alcoholic solution of the reactants in the presence of dilute caustic.

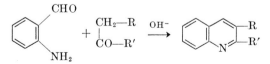

R in the above equation may be H, alkyl, aryl, NO_2, etc., and R' may be H, alkyl, aryl, or COOH.[2] The reaction is restricted by the difficulty of preparing substituted o-aminobenzaldehydes.

The preparation of 6,7-dimethoxyquinoline[3] (III) by a modified procedure is illustrated as follows:

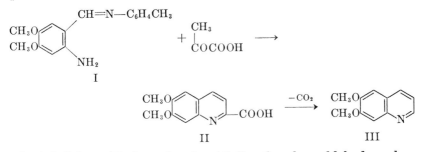

The Schiff base (I) from 2-amino-4,5-dimethoxybenzaldehyde and p-toluidine is allowed to react with pyruvic acid, and the resulting quinaldic acid (II) may be decarboxylated to yield 6,7-dimethoxyquinoline (III).

Strong base anion-exchange resins such as Amberlite IRA-400, and Dowex 2 have been found to be effective and convenient catalysts for the Friedländer reaction.[4] It was also found that the base-catalyzed condensation of o-aminobenzaldehyde with formylacetone dimethyl acetal leads to the benzylidene derivative (IV) which was converted

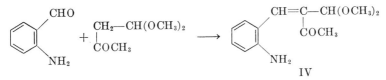

into 3-acetylquinoline by treatment with acid.

References

1. P. Friedländer, *Ber. deut. Chem. Ges.* **15**, 2572 (1882).
2. R. C. Elderfield, ed., *in* "Heterocyclic Compounds," Vol. 4, pp. 45–47. Wiley, New York, 1952.
3. W. Borsche and W. Ried, *Ann. Chem. Liebigs* **554**, 269 (1943).
4. S. Yamada and I. Chibata, *Pharm. Bull.* (*Tokyo*) **3**, 21, (1955).

Fries Reaction

Karl Fries (1875–   ) was born in Kiedrich on the Rhine. He studied at Darmstadt and then under Zincke at Marburg, where he obtained the Ph.D. degree in 1899. Fries joined the faculty at Marburg and in 1912 was promoted to associate professor. Six years later he was called to direct the Chemical Institute at the Technische Hochschule of Braunschweig.

One of Fries' recent interests was concerned with an investigation of bicyclic compounds, such as benzothiazoles, benzoxazoles, thionaphthenes, and indazoles, and their comparison with naphthalene.

The preparation of phenolic ketones by the rearrangement of phenolic esters in the presence of aluminum chloride is called the Fries reaction.[1,2] The general reaction is illustrated as follows, where R is either an aliphatic or aromatic radical.

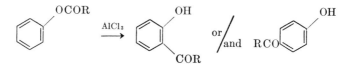

The migration of the acyl group to the *ortho* or *para* position depends to a large extent upon the experimental conditions and structure of the ester. In many instances, a mixture of the two isomers is obtained. As a general rule, low temperatures favor the formation of the *para* isomer; high temperatures, the *ortho* isomer. An example is the rearrangement of *m*-cresyl acetate.[3]

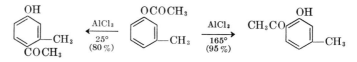

This is consistent with the observation that *p*-hydroxy ketones may be isomerized to the *ortho* isomer by heating with aluminum chloride at elevated temperatures.[4]

When nitrobenzene is employed as a solvent in the Fries reaction, the rearrangement usually proceeds at a lower temperature than in the absence of a solvent. Shah and Shah[5] have investigated the Fries migration of isomeric acetoxybenzoic acids under various conditions. When the *ortho* isomer (I) was added to anhydrous aluminum chloride in nitrobenzene, a vigorous reaction resulted. After one hour, concentrated hydrochloric acid and ice were added to decompose the aluminum chloride salt, and the nitrobenzene was removed by steam distillation. An 83% yield of 5-acetyl-2-hydroxybenzoic acid (II) was obtained.

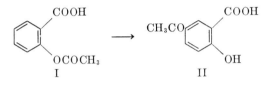

When the reaction was carried out at 120–125° in the absence of nitrobenzene, about half of the above yield was obtained. With the *para* isomer, *p*-acetoxybenzoic acid, a 57% yield of 3-acetyl-4-hydroxybenzoic acid resulted when the rearrangement was performed at 150–155° or at 180–185°. In this case, no rearrangement product was obtained when nitrobenzene was used. The *m*-acetoxybenzoic acid, under various conditions, gave no migration product.

The Fries rearrangement of higher fatty acid esters of *m*-ethylphenol at low temperatures in the presence of nitrobenzene or at high temperatures in the absence of solvent gave only the *o*-hydroxy ketones.[6]

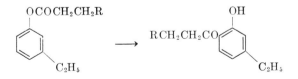

A series of aromatic bis(*o*-hydroxyketones) of the type (III) has been prepared by a double Fries rearrangement starting with di-*p*-

tolyl esters of aliphatic dicarboxylic acids.[7] The reaction was successful for the diacids where $x = (CH_2)_2$ to $(CH_2)_8$.

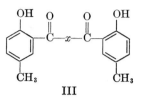

III

References

1. K. Fries and G. Fink, *Ber. deut. Chem. Ges.* **41**, 4271 (1908).
2. A review of the Fries reaction is given by A. H. Blatt, *in* "Organic Reactions" (R. Adams, ed.), Vol. 1, p. 342. Wiley, New York, 1942.
3. K. W. Rosenmund and W. Schnurr, *Ann. Chem. Liebigs* **460**, 56 (1928).
4. Migrations to the *para*-position at high temperatures have been reported; see N. M. Cullinane and B. F. R. Edwards, *J. Chem. Soc.* p. 434 (1958).
5. D. N. Shah and N. M. Shah, *J. Indian Chem. Soc.* **26**, 235 (1949).
6. A. B. Sen and S. S. Tiwari, *J. Indian Chem. Soc.* **29**, 357 (1952).
7. F. D. Thomas, II, M. Shamma, and W. C. Fernelius, *J. Am. Chem. Soc.* **80**, 5864 (1958).

Gabriel Synthesis

Siegmund Gabriel (1851–1924) was born in Berlin, Germany. He studied under Hofmann at Berlin and under Bunsen at Heidelberg, where he received the chemistry Ph.D. degree. Gabriel returned to Berlin as an instructor in the inorganic department under Hofmann. He became a good friend of Emil Fischer, Hofmann's successor at Berlin, and often substituted for Fischer in his lectures. Gabriel had many friends among his students and colleagues. He was vice-president of the German Chemical Society and one of its directors.

Gabriel was interested in a variety of organic problems, including syntheses of cyclic nitrogen compounds. In addition to work in the purine series he prepared ethylenimine[1] and oxazolidone from β-bromoethylamine, and isoquinolines from phthalylglycine esters.[2] He prepared aliphatic and aromatic ketones from phthalylglycine chloride and synthesized quinazoline from o-nitrobenzylamine.

The preparation of primary amines by the reaction of a halo compound with potassium phthalimide followed by hydrolysis of the resulting N-substituted phthalimide is commonly referred to as the Gabriel synthesis. One of the first compounds prepared by Gabriel[3]

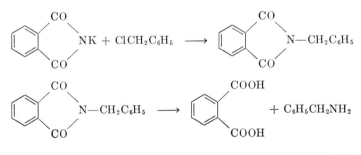

109

by this method was benzylamine. By heating potassium phthalimide with benzyl chloride at 170–180° he obtained benzyl phthalimide. Hydrolysis of this intermediate with fuming hydrochloric acid at 200° yielded phthalic acid and benzylamine.

The Gabriel synthesis has been employed in the preparation of a wide variety of amino compounds, including aliphatic amines, aliphatic diamines, and amino acids. The method offers an unequivocal synthesis of a primary amine.

A modification of the Gabriel synthesis which facilitates the cleavage of the intermediate phthalimido compound was introduced by Ing and Manske in 1926.[4] The N-substituted phthalimides react with hydrazine hydrate to give an intermediate product which is easily decomposed by 10% hydrochloric acid to give phthalyl hydrazide and the primary amine.

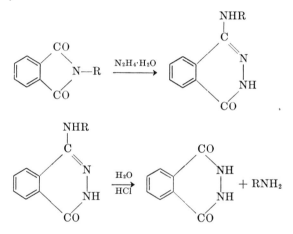

The procedure involves refluxing the phthalimide compounds in alcohol with an equivalent amount of hydrazine hydrate. After the alcohol is removed, the residue is heated with hydrochloric acid on a steam bath. The phthalyl hydrazide is filtered off, leaving the amine hydrochloride in solution. The yields of primary amines obtained by this method are usually very good.

It has been shown[5] that dimethylformamide is an excellent solvent for the condensation of potassium phthalimide with an organic halide. With a reactive halide such as phenacyl bromide, the reaction in dimethylformamide is exothermal, and complete in ten minutes. The

110

yield of phthalimidoacetophenone is 92%. The method is applicable to less reactive halides if the reaction temperature is raised.

References

1. S. Gabriel, *Ber. deut. Chem. Ges.* **21**, 1049 (1888).
2. S. Gabriel and J. Colman, *Ber. deut. Chem. Ges.* **33**, 980, 2630 (1900).
3. S. Gabriel, *Ber. deut. Chem. Ges.* **20**, 224 (1887).
4. H. R. Ing and R. H. F. Manske, *J. Chem. Soc.* p. 2348 (1926).
5. J. C. Sheehan and W. A. Bolhofer, *J. Am. Chem. Soc.* **72**, 2786 (1950).

Gattermann Aldehyde Synthesis

Ludwig Gattermann (1860–1921) was born in Goslar, Germany. He began his training in chemistry at Heidelberg and later studied under Liebermann and his assistant Jacobsen at the Gewerbe Akademie in Berlin (1882). Gattermann continued his studies at Göttingen, where he obtained his Ph.D. in 1885. There he was instructed by Sandmeyer, whom he succeeded, to become lecture assistant to Victor Meyer. When Meyer went to Heidelberg in 1889 to succeed Bunsen, he took Gattermann with him. In 1900, Gattermann was appointed head of the department at Freiburg.

Gattermann's textbook, "Die Praxis der organischen Chemie," (1894) was one of his major contributions to the field of organic chemistry. He worked on the preparation and purification of the explosive nitrogen trichloride, for which he attracted a great deal of publicity. In addition to his work on the modification of the Sandmeyer reaction and anthraquinone dyes, Gattermann developed several methods for the synthesis of aromatic aldehydes.

The preparation of phenolic aldehydes or their ethers by the condensation of phenols and phenolic ethers with hydrogen cyanide in the presence of hydrogen chloride and zinc chloride (or aluminum chloride) is known as the Gattermann aldehyde synthesis.[1,2] The reaction may be illustrated by the preparation of *p*-anisaldehyde from anisole.

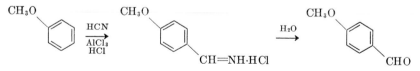

A solution of anisole and anhydrous hydrogen cyanide in ether is saturated with hydrogen chloride, and aluminum chloride is added. The aldimine hydrochloride, which can be isolated, is hydrolyzed by heating in aqueous solution. The yields in the Gattermann reaction are generally good.

A modification of the Gattermann synthesis in which the hydrogen cyanide was replaced by zinc cyanide was introduced by Adams and Levine.[3] The yields of hydroxy aldehydes obtained with this safer and more convenient reagent are usually similar to those obtained by the hydrogen cyanide procedure.

Another modification of the Gattermann reaction is the use of aluminum chloride dissolved in ether.[4] By this procedure methyl 2,4-dihydroxy-3-formylbenzoate (II) was readily prepared in 70% yield from methyl β-resorcylate (I).

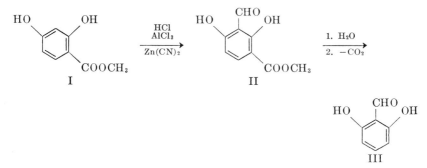

The reaction was unsuccessful under the usual conditions of the Gattermann synthesis. Hydrolysis of the ester (II) followed by decarboxylation yielded γ-resorcylaldehyde, a compound not readily obtained by other methods. Whalley[5] applied this modified reaction for the preparation of the corresponding 6-methyl derivative, methyl 2,4-dihydroxy-3-formyl-6-methylbenzoate.

An alternative method for the direct introduction of an aldehyde group into aromatic compounds involves the use of phosphorus oxychloride, and N-methylformanilide or dimethylformamide. The procedure which has been referred to as the *Vilsmeier reaction*,[6] is limited to activated compounds. It has been successfully employed in the direct formylation of aromatic hydrocarbons such as anthracene and pyrene, and heterocyclic compounds including thiophene, pyrrole, and indole.

Jutz[7] has prepared some unsaturated aldehydes by the Vilsmeier procedure with vinylogues of N-methylformamide. For example, with N-methylanilinopropenal (IV, R = C_6H_5, R' = CH_3), phosphorus oxy-

113

chloride and dimethylaniline (V) the product is *p*-dimethylaminocin-namaldehyde. The reaction is pictured as follows:

$$RR'NCH=CHCHO + POCl_3 \longrightarrow [RR'NCH=CH-\overset{+}{C}HOPOCl_2]Cl^- \overset{(V)}{\longrightarrow}$$
$$IV$$

$$(CH_3)_2N-\underset{}{\bigcirc}-CH=CH-CH=\overset{+}{N}RR' \overset{OH^-}{\longrightarrow}$$

$$(CH_3)_2N-\underset{}{\bigcirc}-CH=CH-CHO + NHRR'$$

The intermediate anil could be isolated as a crystalline perchlorate.

The reaction of a variety of amides with phosphorus oxychloride, phosgene, and thionyl chloride has been carried out in connection with an investigation of the mechanism of the *Vilsmeier reaction*.[8] The stabilities of the resulting products are recorded. These adducts are represented as amido- or imidochlorides.

$$[RR'N-\overset{+}{C}H-Cl]PO_2Cl_2^-$$

References

1. L. Gattermann, *Ber. deut. Chem. Ges.* **31**, 1149 (1898); L. Gattermann and W. Berchelmann, *Ber. deut. Chem. Ges.* **31**, 1765 (1898); L. Gattermann and M. Köbner, *Ber. deut. Chem. Ges.* **32**, 278 (1899).
2. A review of the Gattermann aldehyde synthesis is given by W. E. Truce, *in* "Organic Reactions" (R. Adams, ed.), Vol. IX, p. 37. Wiley, New York, 1957.
3. R. Adams and I. Levine, *J. Am. Chem. Soc.* **45**, 2373 (1923); also R. T. Arnold and J. Sprung, *J. Am. Chem. Soc.* **60**, 1699 (1938).
4. R. C. Shah and M. C. Laiwalla, *J. Chem. Soc.* p. 1828 (1938).
5. W. B. Whalley, *J. Chem. Soc.* p. 3278 (1949).
6. A. Vilsmeier and A. Haack, *Ber. deut. Chem. Ges.* **60**, 119 (1927); see W. E. Truce, *in* "Organic Reactions" (R. Adams, ed.), Vol. IX, p. 52. Wiley, New York, 1957.
7. C. Jutz, *Chem. Ber.* **91**, 850 (1958).
8. H. H. Bosshard, R. Mory, M. Schmid, and H. Zollinger, *Helv. Chim. Acta* **42**, 1659 (1959).

Gattermann Reaction

The replacement of a diazonium salt by a halo or a cyano group using metallic copper as the catalyst is usually called the Gattermann reaction.[1] An example is the formation of chlorobenzene by adding powdered copper to a solution of benzenediazonium chloride in hydrochloric acid.

$$\text{C}_6\text{H}_5\text{N}_2\text{Cl} \xrightarrow[\text{HCl}]{\text{Cu}} \text{C}_6\text{H}_5\text{Cl} + \text{N}_2$$

Another illustration is the preparation of o-bromotoluene in 47% yield from o-toluidine.[2]

$$\xrightarrow[\text{NaNO}_2]{\text{HBr}} \xrightarrow[\text{HBr}]{\text{Cu}} + \text{N}_2$$

The Gattermann reaction has not been used widely in organic syntheses. The yields obtained are usually lower than with the Sandmeyer reaction,[3] in which a cuprous salt is employed as the catalyst. In addition, the finely-divided copper may interfere with the purification of the product.

References

1. L. Gattermann, *Ber. deut. Chem. Ges.* **23**, 1218 (1890).
2. L. A. Bigelow, *in* "Organic Synthesis" (A. H. Blatt, ed.), Coll. Vol. II, p. 130. Wiley, New York, 1943.
3. See p. 210.

Gattermann-Koch Reaction

The preparation of aromatic aldehydes by the direct introduction of a formyl group by means of carbon monoxide, hydrogen chloride, and a suitable catalyst is known as the Gattermann-Koch reaction.[1,2] The synthesis is a special type of Friedel-Crafts reaction. An example is the formation of p-tolualdehyde from toluene.[3]

$$H_3C \underset{}{\bigcirc} \xrightarrow[\substack{AlCl_3, Cu_2Cl_2 \\ (51\%)}]{CO, HCl} H_3C \underset{}{\bigcirc} CHO$$

The reaction is carried out by passing a mixture of gaseous carbon monoxide and hydrogen chloride into a suspension of cuprous chloride and aluminum chloride in toluene.

When the Gattermann-Koch reaction is conducted at atmospheric pressure, a carrier, cuprous chloride, is usually employed. Its function is believed to be the formation of a complex with carbon monoxide to facilitate the production of formyl chloride. The latter has been suggested as the active species in the Gattermann-Koch reaction.

Dilke and Eley[4] have investigated the reaction for the preparation of benzaldehyde from benzene and carbon monoxide. On the basis of their work they postulated that the HCO^+ ion is involved in the reaction.

$$HCl + CO + AlBr_3 \rightleftharpoons HCO^+ + AlBr_3Cl^-$$

$$HCO^+ + C_6H_6 \longrightarrow C_6H_5CHO + H^+$$

For the most part, aromatic hydrocarbons and alkylated aromatic hydrocarbons have been the common starting materials in the Gattermann-Koch reaction. Strongly electron-attracting groups in the aromatic ring inhibit the reaction. When the synthesis is carried out in an autoclave at elevated pressures, no carrier is necessary. Side reactions, probably due to the presence of the catalyst, may include migration of alkyl groups or dealkylation.

References

1. L. Gattermann and J. A. Koch, *Ber. deut. Chem. Ges.* **30**, 1622 (1897).
2. A review of the Gattermann-Koch reaction is given by N. L. Crounse, *in* "Organic Reactions" (R. Adams, ed.), Vol. V, p. 290. Wiley, New York, 1949.
3. G. H. Coleman and D. Craig, *in* "Organic Syntheses" (A. H. Blatt, ed.), Coll. Vol. II, p. 583. Wiley, New York, 1943.
4. M. H. Dilke and D. D. Eley, *J. Chem. Soc.* pp. 2601, 2613 (1949).

Gomberg-Bachmann-Hey Reaction

Moses Gomberg (1866–1947) was born in Elizabetgrad, Russia. In 1885, the Gomberg family fled from Tzarist Russia and came to the United States. Gomberg completed his high school work in Chicago and then went to the University of Michigan, where he received the Ph.D. degree in 1894. He went abroad to study with von Baeyer in Munich and with Victor Meyer at Heidelberg. He returned to Michigan, where he was appointed professor of chemistry and later (1927) became head of the department.

At Heidelberg, Gomberg began his investigation of polyarylmethyl compounds which led to the discovery of the free radical, triphenylmethyl, a discovery which opened up a new field in organic chemistry. Gomberg received many awards for his outstanding contributions. In 1931 he was president of the American Chemical Society.

* * *

Werner Emanuel Bachmann (1901–1951) was born in Detroit, Michigan. He received his doctorate degree in 1926 from the University of Michigan. He then went to Zurich as a Rockefeller Foundation Fellow and to London and Munich as a Guggenheim Fellow. Bachmann returned to the University of Michigan, where he rose to the position of Moses Gomberg University Professor of Chemistry.

Bachmann's work includes an investigation of free radicals, molecular rearrangements, and the synthesis of sex hormones and explosives.

* * *

Donald Holroyde Hey (1904–   ) was born in Swansea, Wales. He received the M.Sc. degree at the University of Wales, the Ph.D. degree at London (where he was a student of L. E. Hinkel), and the D.Sc. degree at Manchester. Hey served as a lecturer at Manchester and London Universities. From 1941 to 1945 he was director of research at the British Schering Research Institute. He then returned to London University, where he is now Daniell Professor of Chemistry.

The formation of biaryls by treating an aryl diazonium salt solution with sodium hydroxide or sodium acetate in the presence of an aromatic liquid is commonly called the Gomberg reaction. It is also referred to as the Gomberg-Bachmann-Hey reaction.[1,2] An illustration is the reaction of the diazonium salt prepared from p-nitroaniline with benzene to give 4-nitrobiphenyl.[3] Better yields are often ob-

$$O_2N\langle\_\rangle N_2Cl + NaOH + \langle\_\rangle \longrightarrow O_2N\langle\_\rangle-\langle\_\rangle$$

tained by replacing sodium hydroxide with sodium acetate.[2] The use of a stabilized diazonium salt,[4] prepared from p-nitrobenzene-diazonium chloride and naphthalene-1,5-disulfonic acid, in the above reaction, resulted in a 70% yield of 4-nitrobiphenyl. A nitrosoacetyl derivative of the aromatic amine has also been employed in the preparation of unsymmetrical biaryls.[5]

An interesting discussion of the electronic versus free-radical interpretation of the Gomberg reaction is given by Hodgson,[6] and Hey and Waters.[7] Hodgson is of the opinion that the diazonium ion is the reactive reagent.

DeTar[8] has recently reviewed the Pschorr synthesis and related diazonium ring-closure reactions. A comparison with the Gomberg synthesis is included.

References

1. M. Gomberg and W. E. Bachmann, *J. Am. Chem. Soc.* **46**, 2339 (1924).
2. J. Elks, J. W. Haworth, and D. H. Hey, *J. Chem. Soc.* p. 1284 (1940).
3. A review of the reaction is given by W. E. Bachmann and R. A. Hoffmann, in "Organic Reactions" (R. Adams, ed.), Vol. II, p. 224. Wiley, New York, 1944.
4. H. H. Hodgson and E. Marsden, *J. Chem. Soc.* p. 208 (1940).
5. W. S. M. Grieve and D. H. Hey, *J. Chem Soc.* p. 1797 (1934); H. France, I. M. Heilbron, and D. H. Hey, *J. Chem. Soc.* p. 369 (1940).
6. H. H. Hodgson, *J. Soc. Dyers Colourists* **65**, 347 (1949).
7. D. H. Hey and W. A. Waters, *J. Soc. Dyers Colourists* **64**, 359 (1948).
8. DeLos F. DeTar, in "Organic Reactions" (R. Adams, ed.), Vol. IX, p. 409. Wiley, New York, 1957.

Gould-Jacobs Reaction

R. Gordon Gould (1909–   ) was born in Chicago, Illinois. He studied at Harvard University, where he was awarded the Ph.D. degree in 1933. After serving as an instructor at Harvard and Iowa, he went to the Rockefeller Institute for Medical Research. In 1947 he was appointed associate professor of biochemistry at the Illinois Medical School.

* * *

Walter A. Jacobs (1883–   ) was born in New York City. He studied at Columbia University, where he received the A.B. and A.M. degrees, and then at Berlin, where he obtained the Ph.D. degree in 1907. He then became associated with the Rockefeller Institute for Medical Research, where he became a member in 1923 and a member emeritus in 1949. One of Jacobs' main interests has been the investigation of natural products.

The formation of 4-hydroxyquinolines starting with an aromatic amine and ethoxymethylenemalonic ester (EMME) is referred to as the Gould-Jacobs reaction.[1] Price and Roberts[2] have developed this method for the preparation of intermediates in the synthesis of chemotherapeutic agents, especially antimalarials. The process involves the following steps:

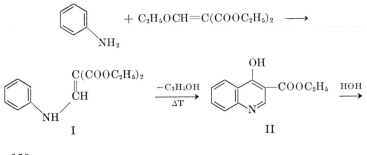

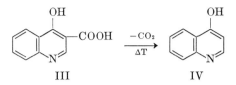

III   IV

Condensation of m-chloroaniline with ethoxymethylenemalonic ester gives α-carbethoxy-β-anilinoacrylate (I), which is cyclized by pyrolysis in Dowtherm A to the 3-quinolinecarboxylate (II). Hydrolysis of this ester to the corresponding acid (III) followed by decarboxylation gives the 4-hydroxyquinoline (IV).

A large number of hydroxyquinolines with different substituents in the benzenoid ring have been prepared by the EMME process.[3] The method is a very satisfactory one and usually gives good yields. With *meta*-substituted anilines, the main product is usually the 7-substituted 4-hydroxyquinoline. An example is the preparation of 7-chloro-4-hydroxyquinoline in 60% yield from m-chloroaniline and ethoxymethylenemalonic ester.[4] This yield is much higher than that obtained by the Conrad-Limpach synthesis (p. 59). In this case, a significant amount of the isomeric 5-chloro-4-hydroxyquinoline is produced.

References

1. R. G. Gould and W. A. Jacobs, *J. Am. Chem. Soc.* **61**, 2890 (1939).
2. C. C. Price and R. M. Roberts, *J. Am. Chem Soc.* **68**, 1204 (1946).
3. R. H. Reitsma, *Chem. Revs.* **43**, 43 (1948); R. C. Elderfield, ed., *in* "Heterocyclic Compounds," Vol. 4, pp. 38–40. Wiley, New York, 1952.
4. C. C. Price and R. M. Roberts, *in* "Organic Syntheses" (H. R. Snyder, ed.), Vol. 28, p. 38. Wiley, New York, 1948.

Graebe-Ullmann Synthesis

Carl Graebe (1841–1927) was born in Frankfurt, Germany. He received his doctor's degree under Bunsen at the University of Heidelberg. He then studied under Kolbe at Marburg. After working for a short time in a dyestuff factory, Graebe went to Erlenmeyer's laboratory to work on his own problems. Next, he served as an assistant to von Baeyer and in 1869 joined the faculty at Leipzig. A year later he assumed the chair in chemistry at Königsberg. After several years he resigned because of poor health and went to Switzerland where, in 1878, he was appointed professor of chemistry at the University of Geneva. He retired in 1906 to return to Frankfurt.

Graebe is probably best known for his work with Liebermann on the structure determination and synthesis of the plant dye, alizarin. With Liebermann he showed that anthracene is formed by the reduction of alizarin. Graebe discovered acridine and carbazole in coal tar. He prepared phthalic acid from naphthalene and demonstrated the bicyclic nature of the latter. He also worked on quinones, acenaphthene, picene, and fluorene. Graebe's fame was widespread. He received the Perkin, Lavoisier, and Berthollet medals.

Graebe and Ullmann[1] found that, when o-aminodiphenylamine was diazotized and the resulting 1-phenylbenzotriazole heated, nitrogen was evolved and carbazole was obtained in excellent yield.[2]

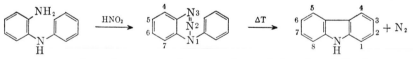

The Graebe-Ullmann synthesis is limited by the difficulties in preparing derivatives of o-aminodiphenylamine and also by the inhibitory effect of electron-attracting groups on the aromatic ring.

Coker and associates[3] investigated the effect of different substituents on the formation of carbazoles by the Graebe-Ullmann synthesis. They succeeded in preparing 3- and 1-chloro-6-nitro-carbazoles but were unsuccessful with certain other benzotriazoles. Several 6-cyanocarbazoles were also synthesized. For example, 3-chloro-6-cyanocarbazole was prepared by the following sequence of reactions starting with p-chloroaniline and 4-chloro-3-nitro-benzonitrile.

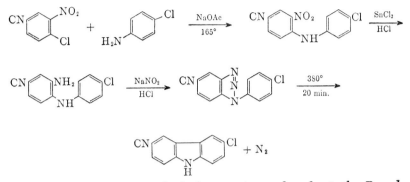

A more satisfactory method of preparing carbazoles is the *Borsche synthesis*,[4] which involves the reaction of a phenylhydrazine with cyclohexanone.

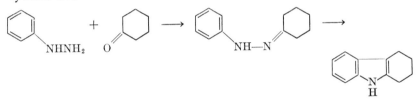

The tetrahydrocarbazoles which are obtained in this synthesis may be dehydrogenated by a variety of methods. Lead dioxide, palladous chloride, palladium black with cinnamic acid, and chloranil have been used for this purpose.[2]

References

1. C. Graebe and F. Ullmann, *Ann. Chem. Liebigs* **291**, 16 (1896).
2. For a review of the chemistry of carbazole, see N. Campbell and B. Barclay, *Chem. Revs.* **43**, 53 (1948); see also, W. Freudenberg, *in* "Heterocyclic Compounds" (R. C. Elderfield, ed.), Vol. 3, p. 298. Wiley, New York, 1952. For a review of the Pschorr synthesis and related diazonium ring closure reactions, see DeLos F. DeTar, *in* "Organic Reactions" (R. Adams, ed.), Vol. IX, p. 409. Wiley, New York, 1957.
3. G. G. Coker, S. G. P. Plant, and P. B. Turner, *J. Chem. Soc.* p. 110 (1951).
4. W. Borsche, *Ann. Chem. Liebigs* **359**, 49 (1908).

Grignard Reaction

Victor Grignard (1871–1935) was born in Cherbourg, France. After studying for one year with L. Bouveault, he worked for his doctorate under P. A. Barbier at Lyons. At the suggestion of Barbier, Grignard began an investigation of the use of magnesium in condensation reactions. He soon found that an alkyl halide reacted readily with magnesium in absolute ether and that it was desirable to allow this reaction to proceed to completion before carrying out any subsequent reactions. In 1901, Grignard submitted his thesis on the mixed organomagnesium compounds and their application to the synthesis of acids, alcohols, and hydrocarbons. The importance of this fundamental discovery is known to every chemist. Grignard continued his research on organomagnesium compounds at Lyons and later at Nancy, where he became professor of organic chemistry. In 1919, he returned to Lyons to succeed Barbier as head of the department of general chemistry.

In 1912, Grignard shared the Nobel Prize for chemistry with P. Sabatier.

The reaction of a halogen compound with magnesium in ether to form a solution of an organomagnesium compound (Grignard reagent) which is brought into reaction with a second component is known as the Grignard reaction. The Grignard reagent reacts with almost all functional groups.[1,2]

The formulation of the reaction in the preparation of a tertiary alcohol was first given by Barbier,[3] who carried out the reaction with both components present.

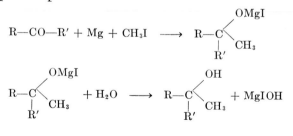

124

In the Grignard reaction two steps are involved: (1) formation of the Grignard reagent: $RX + Mg \rightarrow RMgX$; (2) reaction with a second component.

The recent use of tetrahydrofuran or ethers of di- and triethylene-glycol as solvents has extended the scope of the Grignard reaction. The enhanced activity of organic halides in these solvents is attributed to the availability of π-electrons of the oxygen atom of the ether for co-ordination with magnesium.

The Grignard reagents from vinyl halides and magnesium are readily prepared in tetrahydrofuran or di- or triethyleneglycol ethers. The reaction of vinylmagnesium bromide and acid anhydrides has been carried out in tetrahydrofuran at $-60°$ to $-70°$ to give the vinyl ketones in 60–80% yield.[4]

$$2CH_2{=}CHMgBr + 2(RCO)_2O \longrightarrow$$
$$2CH_2{=}CHCOR + MgBr_2 + Mg(OCOR)_2$$

Hawthorne[5] has recently reported the conversion of aryl halides to phenols by treatment of the Grignard reagent with trimethylborate followed by oxidation of the resulting mixture with hydrogen peroxide.

References

1. For references to Grignard's works see "Fifty years of the Grignard reaction," H. Rheinbolt, *J. Chem. Educ.* **27**, 476 (1950) and the Grignard anniversary number of the *Bull. soc. chim. France* pp. 897–932 (1950).
2. A review of the Grignard reaction is given by M. S. Kharasch and O. Reinmuth, "Grignard Reactions of Non-Metallic Substances." Constable, London, 1954.
3. P. A. Barbier, *Compt. rend. acad. sci.* **128**, 110 (1899).
4. G. Martin, *Compt. rend. acad. sci.* **245**, 1933 (1957).
5. M. F. Hawthorne, *J. Org. Chem.* **22**, 1001 (1957).

Hantzsch Pyridine Synthesis

Arthur Rudolf Hantzsch (1857–1935) was born in Dresden, Germany. He studied chemistry under R. Schmidt, who is probably best known for his work on the Kolbe reaction. He continued his studies under Wislicenus at Würzburg and received his doctor's degree in 1880. Next he worked in Hofmann's laboratory in Berlin, and from there joined the faculty at Leipzig, where he published his work on the syntheses of pyridine compounds from acetoacetic ester and aldehydes. His reputation as an outstanding chemist won him an appointment as full professor in the Polytechnicum in Zurich. There, Hantzsch and A. Werner (1866–1919) presented their theory regarding the stereochemistry of nitrogen and the structure of oximes. In 1893, he succeeded Emil Fischer at Würzburg and, in 1903, Wislicenus at Leipzig.

During his career Hantzsch published about 450 papers. They include his pioneer work on the stereoisomerism of diazo compounds, the relationship of color and constitution of dyes, and the syntheses of pyridines, thiazoles, and coumarones.

The formation of pyridine derivatives from the condensation of two moles of a β-keto ester with an aldehyde and ammonia is known as the Hantzsch pyridine synthesis.[1]

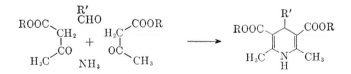

The dihydropyridine obtained in the reaction is readily oxidized to the pyridine derivative.

There have been many modifications of the Hantzsch synthesis[2] in which cyanoacetic esters, malonic esters, and diketones have been employed. The intermediate in the above reaction, β-aminocrotonic ester, has also been used as a starting material. In many instances it has been found desirable to isolate the intermediates in the synthesis.

In view of its many possible variations, the Hantzsch synthesis has been employed for the preparation of a very large number of pyridine derivatives. An example is the condensation of ethoxyacetyl-acetone with cyanoacetamide in the presence of piperidine to give 3-cyano-4-ethoxymethyl-2-hydroxy-6-methylpyridine, an intermediate in the synthesis of vitamin B_6.[3]

Another example is the formation of 4-substituted ethyl 5-cyano-1,4-dihydro-2,6-dimethylnicotinate from the reaction of an aryl alde-hyde with β-aminocrotononitrile and ethyl β-aminocrotonate.[4]

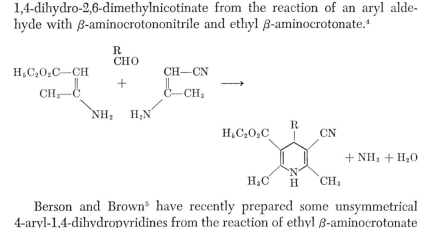

Berson and Brown[5] have recently prepared some unsymmetrical 4-aryl-1,4-dihydropyridines from the reaction of ethyl β-aminocrotonate with an arylidene acetylacetone. The mechanism for the formation of the Hantzsch synthesis products has been evaluated.

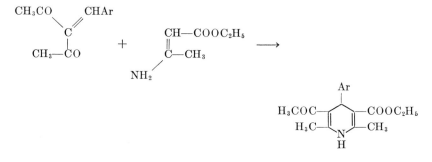

References

1. A. Hantzsch, *Ann. Chem. Liebigs* **215**, 1 (1882).
2. A discussion of the Hantzsch pyridine synthesis and its modifications is given by H. S. Mosher, *in* "Heterocyclic Compounds" (R. C. Elderfield, ed.), Vol. 1, pp. 462–472. Wiley, New York, 1950.
3. S. A. Harris and K. Folkers, *J. Am. Chem. Soc.* **61**, 1245 (1939).
4. V. A. Petrow, *J. Chem. Soc.* p. 884 (1946).
5. J. A. Berson and E. Brown, *J. Am. Chem. Soc.* **77**, 444 (1955).

Hell-Volhard-Zelinsky Reaction

Carl Magnus von Hell (1849–1926) was born in Stuttgart, Germany. He studied at Stuttgart under Fehling and at Munich under Erlenmeyer. After serving in the War of 1870, during which he became very ill, von Hell returned to Stuttgart as an assistant to Fehling, whom he succeeded in 1883.

In 1889, von Hell synthesized the paraffin hydrocarbon, $C_{60}H_{122}$, which was the highest alkane known at that time. He is probably best known for his procedure for the bromination of acids in the presence of phosphorus.

* * *

Jacob Volhard (1834–1909) was born in Darmstadt, Germany. He received his doctor's degree in 1855 at Giessen, where he studied under Liebig and then under Will. He studied under Bunsen at Heidelberg for one year then received an assistantship at Munich to work with Liebig. From 1860 to 1861 Volhard served as an assistant to Hofmann in London. After spending a short time in Kolbe's laboratory in Marburg, he returned to Munich, where he became an associate professor. When von Baeyer succeeded Liebig, Volhard became director of the inorganic and analytical departments. During this period he worked on his well-known volumetric determinations.

Volhard synthesized sarcosine (1862), guanidine, and creatine. With Erdmann (1885) he published a synthesis of thiophene and derivatives from succinic acids. The need for α-bromo acids in this work led to the bromination procedure, which was an improvement over von Hell's method. Volhard was also interested in the synthesis of diphenylacetic acid esters.

* * *

Nikolai D. Zelinsky (1861–1953) was born in Tyraspol, Russia. He studied at Odessa, at Leipzig, and at Göttingen, where he was

129

a student of Victor Meyer. He received his Ph.D. degree in 1889 at Odessa and became an assistant professor. In 1893, Zelinsky was appointed professor at the University of Moscow, where he became head of the department of organic chemistry. Zelinsky was a member of the U.S.S.R. Academy of Sciences. He was awarded the title of Hero of Socialist Labor in 1945, and in 1951 he celebrated his ninetieth birthday and received the Order of Lenin.

During his long and fruitful career, Zelinsky published about 500 papers. Many of these contributions deal with the study of catalytic hydrogenations, dehalogenations, terpene chemistry, and synthetic rubber.

The preparation of α-chloro or α-bromo acids by the treatment of aliphatic carboxylic acids with chlorine or bromine usually in the presence of a small amount of the corresponding phosphorus trihalide is known as the Hell-Volhard-Zelinsky reaction.[1,2] The formation of the acyl halide probably precedes halogenation, since it is known that halogens react more rapidly with acyl halides than with the acids themselves. The steps in the reaction may be formulated as follows:

$$3RCH_2COOH + PX_3 \longrightarrow 3RCH_2COX + H_3PO_3$$

$$RCH_2COX + X_2 \longrightarrow RCHXCOX + HX$$

$$RCHXCOX + RCH_2COOH \longrightarrow RCHXCOOH + RCH_2COX$$

The original Hell-Volhard procedure which involves the use of bromine and phosphorus probably proceeds also via the acyl bromide.

An example of the bromination with phosphorus trichloride is the preparation of α-bromoisocaproic acid.[3]

$$(CH_3)_2CHCH_2CH_2COOH \xrightarrow[\substack{PCl_3 \\ (66\%)}]{Br_2} (CH_3)_2CHCH_2CHBrCOOH$$

Attempts to brominate β-bromopropionic acid by the Hell-Volhard-Zelinsky method gave only β-bromopropionyl bromide.[4]

An excellent procedure for the preparation of mono α-bromo derivatives of dicarboxylic acids has been described by Schwenk and Papa.[5] The method involves treating the half-ester of dicarboxylic acids with thionyl chloride and then bromine. The bromo acid chloride thus obtained is treated with ethanol to give the bromo diester which can be purified by distillation.

$$\text{ROOC(CH}_2)_n\text{CH}_2\text{COOH} \xrightarrow{\text{SOCl}_2} \text{ROOC(CH}_2)_n\text{CH}_2\text{COCl} \xrightarrow{\text{Br}_2}$$

$$\text{ROOC(CH}_2)_n\text{CHBrCOCl} \xrightarrow{\text{R'OH}} \text{ROOC(CH}_2)_n\text{CHBrCOOR'}$$

Ethyl α-bromoadipate was obtained in 90% yield by this method.

The procedure is also very satisfactory with monocarboxylic acids and has given practically quantitative yields of ethyl α-bromocyclo-hexylacetate and ethyl α-bromophenylacetate.

References

1. C. Hell, *Ber. deut. Chem. Ges.* **14,** 891 (1881); J. Volhard, *Ann. Chem. Liebigs* **242,** 141 (1887); N. Zelinsky, *Ber. deut. Chem. Ges.* **20,** 2026 (1887).
2. H. B. Watson, *Chem. Revs.* **7,** 180 (1930).
3. C. S. Marvel, *in* "Organic Syntheses" (N. L. Drake, ed.), Vol. 21, p. 74. Wiley, New York, 1941.
4. E. H. Charlesworth and H. J. Anderson, *Can. J. Research* **28B,** 1 (1950).
5. E. Schwenk and D. Papa, *J. Am. Chem. Soc.* **70,** 3626 (1948).

Hoesch Synthesis

Kurt Hoesch (1882–1932) was born in Kreuzau, Germany. He studied at Berlin under Emil Fischer, with whom he worked on the synthesis of the naturally-occurring orsellinic and everninic acids. During World War I, Hoesch was professor of chemistry at the University of Istanbul. After the war he gave up his scientific activities to devote himself to the management of a family business.

In 1915 Hoesch[1] described a method for the preparation of phenolic ketones which involves the condensation of a phenol or phenolic ether with a nitrile in the presence of hydrogen chloride and zinc chloride. For example, when a mixture of resorcinol, acetonitrile, and zinc chloride in ether was saturated with dry hydrogen chloride, a product separated which on heating in aqueous solution gave 2,4-dihydroxyacetophenone.

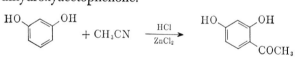

With phloroglucinol and benzonitrile, 2,4,6-trihydroxybenzophenone was obtained.

The Hoesch synthesis,[2] which is a modification of the Gattermann aldehyde synthesis (p. 112), is especially useful in the preparation of polyhydroxyaryl ketones.

A variety of aliphatic and aromatic nitriles have been used in the Hoesch reaction. Zinc chloride and aluminum chloride are the catalysts most often employed. The synthesis is usually represented as involving the formation of a ketimine hydrochloride which may be isolated. Hydrolysis of this product in water gives the ketone.

132

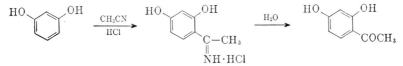

Whalley[3] investigated the Hoesch reaction with trifluoro- and trichloroacetonitriles. When a solution of resorcinol in ether containing zinc chloride was saturated at —5° with hydrogen chloride and trifluoroacetonitrile was added, a solid separated which on hydrolysis with water yielded ω-trifluoro-2,4-dihydroxyacetophenone.

Trichloroacetonitrile does not react with resorcinol, orcinol, pyrogallol, or phloroglucinol, but does with phloroglucinol monomethyl ether to give ω-trichloro-2,4-dihydroxy-6-methoxyacetophenone. By warming a sodium bicarbonate solution of this ketone, chloroform and 2,4-dihydroxy-6-methoxybenzoic acid were obtained.

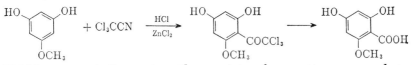

Trichloroacetonitrile reacts with a variety of aromatic compounds to give the ketimine hydrochloride which on acid hydrolysis yields the expected ketone. However, alkaline hydrolysis gives a nitrile in good yield. This is known as the *Houben-Fischer synthesis*.[4]

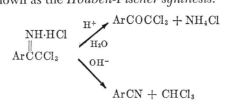

References

1. K. Hoesch, *Ber. deut. Chem. Ges.* **48**, 1122 (1915).
2. A review of the Hoesch synthesis is given by P. E. Spoerri and A. S. DuBois *in* "Organic Reactions" (R. Adams, ed.), Vol. V, p. 387. Wiley, New York, 1949.
3. W. B. Whalley, *J. Chem. Soc.* p. 665 (1951).
4. J. Houben and W. Fischer, *J. prakt. Chem.* **123**, 313 (1929); see also, D. T. Mowry, *Chem. Revs.* **42**, 221 (1948).

Hofmann Reaction

August Wilhelm Hofmann (1818–1892) was born in Giessen, Germany. At the University there he studied under Liebig and received the doctorate degree in 1841. Hofmann continued at Giessen as an assistant to Liebig until 1845, when he was appointed professor at the new Royal College of Chemistry in London. Among his students were W. H. Perkin and P. Griess, the discoverer of the diazo reaction of primary aromatic amines. In 1865, Hofmann became professor at the University of Berlin, where he continued his prolific work.

Hofmann's work on aniline and benzene is commonly regarded as the beginning of the coal-tar dye industry. His preparation of amines and their classification, his studies in the alkaloid field, and his work on the degradation of quaternary bases represent only a portion of his notable contributions to organic chemistry. Hofmann's influence as a teacher was widespread. He was president of the German Chemical Society and received the Copley Medal in 1875.

The preparation of a primary amine by the elimination of the carbonyl group of an amide is known as the Hofmann reaction. The reaction, which was discovered by Hofmann in 1881,[1] involves treatment of the amide with a hypohalite solution. It is formulated as follows:

$$RCONH_2 + X_2 + 2NaOH \longrightarrow RNH_2 + 2NaX + CO_2 + H_2O$$

The isocyanate (RNCO) is the primary product of the reaction; thus, when alcohol is employed as a solvent, a urethan is formed which can be hydrolyzed to the amine. In the above reaction R can be an alkyl, aryl, aralkyl, or heteroaryl group, and X is either chlorine or bromine. The Hofmann reaction proceeds smoothly, and the yields obtained are usually excellent.[2]

The mechanism of the reaction has been the subject of considerable investigation. The first step involves the formation of an N-haloamide (a) which reacts with alkali to give an unstable salt (b). The latter is ionized (c) to form the intermediate (I) which rearranges to an isocyanate (d).

$$\text{(a)} \quad RCONH_2 \xrightarrow{\text{NaOX}} RCONHX$$

$$\text{(b)} \quad RCONHX \xrightarrow{\text{OH}^-} [RCONX]^- + H_2O$$

$$\text{(c)} \quad [RCONX]^- \longrightarrow [R\overset{..}{C}O\overset{..}{N}:] + X^-$$
$$\text{I}$$

$$\text{(d)} \quad R-\overset{\overset{\displaystyle O}{\|}}{C}-\overset{..}{N}: \longrightarrow R-N=C=O$$

The intermediate (I) has also been described as a π complex.[3]

$$\begin{array}{c} {}^-N\!=\!C\!=\!O \\ \downarrow \\ R^+ \end{array}$$

Hydrolysis of the isocyanate by alkali gives the primary amine.

$$R-N=C=O \xrightarrow{\text{OH}^-} RNH_2$$

The rate-controlling step in the reaction appears to be the ionization to form I. In this connection, it has been shown that, with a series of substituted benzamides,[4] the more positive the carbon atom of the carbonyl group, the slower is the reaction. The reaction always proceeds without stereochemical inversion of the migrating group. That R retains its original configuration may be detected by rearranging an amide having an optically-active center adjacent to the carbonyl group and observing retention of optical integrity.

An investigation of the Hofmann reaction with perfluoroamides has shown that either of two products may be obtained depending upon the conditions of the reaction.[5] Pyrolysis of the intermediate anhydrous salt $(C_3F_7CONBr)^-Na^+$ gave the expected isocyanate C_3F_7NCO. However, in aqueous sodium hydroxide solution an isocyanate ion is lost and bromoheptafluoropropane, C_3F_7Br, was obtained.

In the Hofmann reaction with long-chain fatty acid amides a cosolvent such as dioxane was shown to be effective in minimizing side reactions.[6] Improved results were obtained with this solvent with the amides from caprolamide through lauramide.

135

References

1. A. W. Hofmann, *Ber. deut. Chem. Ges.* **14**, 2725 (1881).
2. For a review of the Hofmann reaction, see E. S. Wallis and J. F. Lane, *in* "Organic Reactions" (R. Adams, ed.), Vol. III, p. 267. Wiley, New York, 1946.
3. See M. J. S. Dewar, "Electronic Theory of Organic Chemistry," p. 222, Oxford Univ. Press, London and New York, 1949.
4. C. R. Hauser and W. B. Renfrow, *J. Am. Chem. Soc.* **59**, 121 (1937).
5. D. A. Barr and R. N. Haszeldine, *J. Chem. Soc.* p. 30 (1957).
6. E. Magnien and R. Baltzly, *J. Org. Chem.* **23**, 2029 (1958).

Hofmann Degradation

The decomposition of quaternary ammonium hydroxides to give an olefin and a tertiary amine is known as the Hofmann degradation or exhaustive methylation process.[1] It can be illustrated by the conversion of ethylamine to ethylene and trimethylamine.

$$C_2H_5NH_2 \xrightarrow{CH_3I} C_2H_5N(CH_3)_3I \xrightarrow[H_2O]{Ag_2O} C_2H_5N(CH_3)_3OH \xrightarrow{\Delta T}$$

$$C_2H_4 + N(CH_3)_3 + H_2O$$

The quaternary salt is usually decomposed with moist silver oxide. The reaction is not applicable to pyridines, quinolines, isoquinolines, and hydrogenated quinolines.

Where several different substituents are attached to the nitrogen atom, decomposition of the quaternary ammonium hydroxide will yield an olefin which has the smallest number of alkyl groups attached to it (Hofmann's rule). For example, ethylene is formed from ethyl-propyldimethylammonium hydroxide.

$$\left[CH_3CH_2 - \underset{\underset{CH_3}{|}}{\overset{\overset{CH_3}{|}}{N}} - CH_2CH_2R \right] OH \longrightarrow CH_2{=}CH_2 + N(CH_3)_2CH_2CH_2R$$

This has been explained by hyperconjugation.[2] The inductive effect of the R group would tend to charge the adjacent carbon atom negatively and inhibit the elimination of a β-hydrogen as a proton. It is generally accepted that the Hofmann degradation involves a bimolecular, ionic, *trans* elimination.[3] The mechanism has been pictured by Doering and Meislich[4] as a one-step reaction involving a single transition state.

A quaternary ammonium salt having a phenethyl group may be decomposed by heating with aqueous sodium hydroxide solution.

This can be illustrated with the methiodide of N-(3-methoxybenzyl)-N-methyl-3,4-methylenedioxy-5-methoxyphenethylamine.[5]

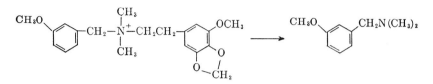

The degradation of the quaternary hydroxides prepared from both cis- and trans-2-phenylcyclohexylamines was shown[6] to give 1-phenylcyclohexene as the sole identifiable product. With the trans-isomer a prototropic shift has been described to account for the product obtained.

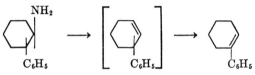

The thermal decomposition of N,N-dimethylalkylamine oxides has been studied by Cope[7] and the products compared with those obtained via the Hofmann reaction. The reaction proceeds with elimination of a cis-β-hydrogen atom and the amine oxide group to give an olefin, and N,N-dimethylhydroxylamine by an intramolecular cyclic mechanism.

$$-\overset{|}{\underset{\underset{H}{|}}{C}}-\overset{|}{\underset{\underset{O}{\downarrow}}{C}}-N(CH_3)_2 \longrightarrow -\overset{|}{C}=\overset{|}{C} + (CH_3)_2NOH$$

In the alicyclic series cyclononyl-, and cyclodecyldimethylamine oxide give trans-cycloölefins. The same is true for the Hofmann reaction. With cycloöctyldimethylamine oxide the product is cis-cycloöctene whereas the quaternary hydroxide leads to a mixture of cis- and trans-compounds. Cis-olefins are obtained by both procedures with the smaller ring compounds.

One of the most important uses of the Hofmann degradation is in structure determination of alkaloids and other complex nitrogen heterocycles. An example is its application in the study of the emetine structure.[8] By a series of Hofmann degradations a nitrogen-free product was obtained which helped elucidate the structure of the alkaloid.

References

1. A. W. Hofmann, *Ber. deut. Chem. Ges.* **14,** 659 (1881).
2. J. W. Baker, "Hyperconjugation," p. 5. Oxford Univ. Press, London and New York, 1952.
3. The factors which influence Hofmann degradation of quaternary ammonium salts particularly in cyclic systems, has been reviewed by K. Jewers and J. McKenna, *J. Chem. Soc.* p. 2209 (1958).
4. W. von E. Doering and H. Meislich, *J. Am. Chem. Soc.* **74,** 2099 (1952).
5. A. R. Surrey, *J. Am. Chem. Soc.* **70,** 2887 (1948).
6. R. T. Arnold and P. N. Richardson, *J. Am. Chem. Soc.* **76,** 3649 (1954).
7. A. C. Cope, D. C. McLean, and N. A. Nelson, *J. Am. Chem. Soc.* **77,** 1628 (1955).
8. A. R. Battersby and H. T. Oppenshaw, *J. Chem. Soc.* pp. 3207, S59 (1949).

Hunsdiecker Reaction

Heinz Hunsdiecker (1904–   ) was born in Cologne, Germany. He studied at the university there and received his doctor's degree in 1930 under Professor Windgen. He took a position as chemist in the firm, Dr. Vogt and Co., where he is now manager and part owner. Hunsdiecker's main interests are in organic syntheses. It was in connection with his work on large-ring ketones and lactones for the perfume industry that he patented the method of making organic halogen compounds which now bears his name.

The formation of halides by the treatment of dry silver salts of carboxylic acids with molar quantities of halogen according to the following equation is usually referred to as the Hunsdiecker reaction.[1,2]

$$RCOOAg + X_2 \longrightarrow RX + CO_2 + AgX$$

Experimental evidence points to a free-radical mechanism for the reaction involving decomposition of an acyl hypohalite.

$$RCOOX \longrightarrow RX + CO_2$$

The silver salts of the carboxylic acids are usually prepared from the acid by treatment with silver nitrate. For high-molecular-weight acids silver oxide has been employed. The dried silver salt is suspended in a suitable solvent such as carbon tetrachloride and the halogen is added. In most cases, bromine is the halogen of choice although satisfactory yields of chlorides have been obtained in some instances where chlorine was used. For the preparation of 1,4-dibromobutane, Schmid[3] found it advantageous to reverse the customary addition, to add the silver salt of adipic acid to bromine in carbon tetrachloride solution.

Other solvents such as benzene, nitrobenzene, and chloroform have also been employed in the Hunsdiecker reaction. The preparation of

140

long-chain alkyl halides is most satisfactory when the reaction is carried out in boiling carbon tetrachloride. On the other hand, low temperatures, below −20°, proved to be optimum for the preparation of cyclobutyl bromide.[4] In this case too, the reverse addition was essential.

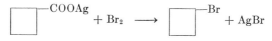

The Hunsdiecker reaction is not suitable for most unsaturated acids. The reaction has been used for the preparation of α,ω-dihalides from the corresponding α,ω-dicarboxylic acids. The best yields are obtained with the higher homologues. Treatment of the silver salts of acid esters leads to ω-haloesters. An example of the latter is the preparation of methyl 5-bromovalerate in 52% yield from methyl hydrogen adipate.[5]

$$CH_3OOC(CH_2)_3CH_2COOAg \xrightarrow{Br_2} CH_3OOC(CH_2)_4Br$$

The silver salts of α-substituted acids lead to a variety of products. For example, α-halogen acids give 1,1-dihalogenated compounds, α-hydroxy and α-amino acids give aldehydes.

$$RCHXCOOAg + X_2 \longrightarrow RCXX' + CO_2 + AgX$$

$$RCHOHCOOAg + X_2 \longrightarrow RCHO + CO_2 + AgX + HX$$

$$RCHNH_2COOAg \xrightarrow[2.\ (H_2O)]{1.\ X_2} RCHO + CO_2 + AgX + NH_4X$$

A recent application of the Hunsdiecker reaction with a heterocyclic compound is the preparation of 4-bromo-1-phenylpyrazole.[6]

The silver salt of the isomeric 3-carboxylic acid is resistant to the reaction.

Simonini reaction.[2,7] When two moles of a silver salt of a carboxylic acid are treated with one mole of iodine the product is an ester.

$$2RCOOAg + I_2 \longrightarrow RCOOR + CO_2 + 2AgI$$

141

The reaction of silver cyclobutanecarboxylate with iodine at 90–100° leads to a mixture of products which have been identified by Roberts and Simmons[8] as cyclobutyl, cyclopropylcarbinyl, and allylcarbinyl cyclobutanecarboxylates.

Prevost reaction.[2,9] The reaction of a silver salt of a carboxylic acid with halogen in the presence of an olefin or acetylene leads to the following products:

$$RCOOAg + X_2 + R'CH{=}CHR'' \longrightarrow R'CH(OCOR)CHXR'' + AgX$$

$$RCOOAg + X_2 + R'C{\equiv}CH \longrightarrow R'C{\equiv}CX + RCO_2H + AgX$$

$$2RCOOAg + X_2 + R'CH{=}CHR'' \longrightarrow$$
$$R'CH(OCOR)CH(OCOR)R'' + 2AgX$$

1,2-Hexadecanediol has been prepared by a Prevost reaction by treatment of silver benzoate with iodine in the presence of 1-hexadecene followed by saponification of the resulting glycol dibenzoate.[10]

References

1. C. Hunsdiecker, H. Hunsdiecker, and E. Vogt, U. S. Patent 2,176,181 (1939); H. Hunsdiecker and C. Hunsdiecker, *Ber. deut. Chem. Ges.* **75**, 291 (1942).
2. A review of the Hunsdiecker and related reactions is given by C. V. Wilson, *in* "Organic Reactions" (R. Adams, ed.), Vol. IX, p. 332. Wiley, New York, 1957.
3. H. Schmid, *Helv. Chim. Acta* **27**, 127 (1944).
4. J. Cason and R. L. Way, *J. Org. Chem.* **14**, 32 (1949).
5. C. F. H. Allen and C. V. Wilson, *in* "Organic Syntheses" (H. Adkins, ed.), Vol. 26, p. 52. Wiley, New York, 1946.
6. E. G. Brain and I. L. Finar, *J. Chem. Soc.* p. 2435 (1958).
7. A. Simonini, *Monatsh. Chem.* **13**, 320 (1892); *Monatsh. Chem.* **14**, 81 (1893).
8. J. D. Roberts and H. E. Simmons, Jr., *J. Am. Chem. Soc.* **73**, 5487 (1951).
9. C. Prevost, *Compt. rend. acad. sci.* **196**, 1129 (1933).
10. C. Niemann and C. D. Wagner, *J. Org. Chem.* **7**, 227 (1942).

Ivanov Reaction

Dimiter Ivanov (1894–   ) was born in Sofia, Bulgaria. He was graduated from the University of Sofia in 1920. He then studied at the University of Nancy (France) where he was awarded the Doctor of Science degree in 1923 under G. Vavon. Ivanov began his teaching career in 1926 at the University of Sofia. He has held the chair of organic chemistry there since 1937.

Ivanov's interests in organic chemistry include organometallic compounds, phosphorus compounds, and essential oils. He is a corresponding member of the Bulgarian Academy of Sciences and head of the section of organic chemistry. In 1932 he became a laureate of the Institut de France.

The reaction of a halomagnesium derivative of a salt of phenylacetic acid (Ivanov reagent) with a carbonyl compound is known as the Ivanov reaction.[1]

$$C_6H_5CH_2-COONa + iso-PrMgCl \longrightarrow C_6H_5CH-COONa + C_3H_8$$

$$\underset{R' \quad COOH}{\underset{|\qquad |}{R-\underset{\underset{|}{}}{C}-CHC_6H_5}} \xleftarrow{RCOR'} \underset{\underset{MgCl}{|}}{}$$

OH

Phenylmalonic acid was prepared in 66% yield by carbonation of the Ivanov reagent.[1] The reaction of the latter with formaldehyde has been reported to give an 83% yield of tropic acid.[2]

The scope of this reaction has been extended by Ivanov with his co-workers, and by Blicke, and others in this country. It has been shown that β,γ-unsaturated aliphatic acid salts may be substituted for phenylacetic acid salts for the preparation of Ivanov reagents.[3] The halomagnesium derivative[4] and the lithium derivative[5] of phenylacetonitrile also react as Ivanov reagents.

143

Ivanov has recently reported that the sodium salt of benzylsulfonic acid forms an Ivanov reagent with isopropylmagnesium chloride which when condensed with benzophenone, give β-hydroxy-α,β,β-triphenylethanesulfonic acid in 64% yield.[6]

$$C_6H_5CH-SO_3Na + C_6H_5COC_6H_5 \longrightarrow$$
$$\underset{MgCl}{|}$$

$$\overset{C_6H_5}{\underset{C_6H_5}{\diagdown}} HO-C-CHC_6H_5 \atop \underset{SO_3H}{|}$$

Blicke and co-workers have used the Ivanov reaction to produce amino alcohols of possible medicinal value. They showed that tertiary amides of phenylacetic acid may be condensed with carbonyl compounds in the Ivanov manner to produce β-hydroxyamides, which give rise to γ-hydroxy tertiary amines when reduced with lithium aluminum hydride.[7] Amino alcohols were also produced when Ivanov reagents were allowed to react with amino-substituted ketones.[8]

The Ivanov reagent is best prepared by the addition of sodium phenylacetate to isopropylmagnesium chloride in ether.[1,9] The reaction with an aldehyde or ketone is carried out in the same manner as with a Grignard reagent.

Zimmerman and Traxler[10] picture the Ivanov reagent as a true enolate. They have shown that this reagent reacts with benzaldehyde to produce predominantly the *threo* isomer.

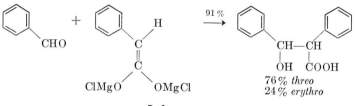

76% *threo*
24% *erythro*

References

1. D. Ivanov and A. Spassov, *Bull. soc. chim. France* [4] **49**, 19, 375 (1931).
2. F. F. Blicke, H. Raffelson, and B. Barna, *J. Am. Chem. Soc.* **74**, 253 (1952).
3. D. Ivanov and G. Pshenchnii, *Compt. rend. acad. sci.* **197**, 1230 (1933).
4. D. Ivanov and I. Paounov, *Compt. rend. acad. sci.* **197**, 923 (1933).
5. D. Ivanov and G. Vasilev, *Compt. rend. acad. bulgare sci.* **10**, 53 (1957).
6. D. Ivanov and N. Marekov, *Croat. Chem. Acta* **29**, 347 (1959).
7. G. S. Dean, *Dissertation Abstr.* **19**, 449 (1958).
8. F. F. Blicke and H. Zinnes, *J. Am. Chem. Soc.* **77**, 5168 (1955).
9. D. Ivanov, *Bull. soc. chim. France* [5] **4**, 682 (1937).
10. H. E. Zimmerman and M. D. Traxler, *J. Am. Chem. Soc.* **79**, 1920 (1957).

Jacobsen Reaction

Oskar Georg Friedrich Jacobsen (1840–1889) was born in Ahrensburg in Holstein and studied at the University of Kiel, where he received the Ph.D. degree in 1868. He served as an assistant at Kiel, and in 1873 was appointed professor of chemistry and pharmacy at the University of Rostock, where he became head of the chemical department, and then president of the university.

The migration of an alkyl group or a halogen atom which results when a polyalkylbenzenesulfonic acid or a halogenated polyalkylbenzenesulfonic acid is treated with concentrated sulfuric acid is known as the Jacobsen reaction.[1,2] The preparation of 2,3,4,5-tetramethylbenzenesulfonic acid from the isomeric 2,3,5,6-tetramethyl compound is an example.

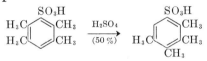

By-products in this reaction are sulfur dioxide, 1,2,4-trimethylbenzenesulfonic acid, and hexamethylbenzene. The sodium salt of the sulfonic acid can be hydrolyzed to yield the hydrocarbon, 1,2,3,4-tetramethylbenzene (prehnitene).[3]

The migration of a halogen atom is illustrated by the rearrangement of 4,6-dichloro-*m*-xylene to 2,4-dichloro-*m*-xylene.

The Jacobsen reaction may involve intramolecular and/or intermolecular migrations. In all cases, vicinal products are obtained. The mechanism of the reaction has not been established.

References

1. O. Jacobsen, *Ber. deut. Chem. Ges.* **19,** 1209 (1886).
2. A review of the reaction is given by L. I. Smith, *in* "Organic Reactions" (R. Adams, ed.), Vol. I, p. 370. Wiley, New York, 1942.
3. L. I. Smith, *in* "Organic Reactions" (R. Adams, ed.), Vol. I, p. 382. Wiley, New York, 1942; see also, S. F. Birch, R. A. Dean, F. A. Fidler, and R. A. Lowry, *J. Am. Chem. Soc.* **71,** 1362 (1949).

Knoevenagel Reaction

Emil Knoevenagel (1865–1921) was born in Hanover, Germany, the son of a chemist. He began his studies at the Technical Institute at Hanover. In 1886 he went to the University of Göttingen, where he studied under Victor Meyer and Gattermann. After receiving the Ph.D. degree in 1889, he accompanied Victor Meyer to Heidelberg, where he became assistant professor of organic chemistry in 1896 and a full professor in 1900.

Knoevenagel was especially interested in the concept of stereoisomerism. He spent a considerable amount of his time investigating the reaction of aldehydes with ethyl acetoacetate in the presence of primary amines. Other interests were in the pyridine series as well as in problems of inorganic and physical chemistry. Knoevenagel showed that pyridine derivatives can be synthesized by heating 1,5-diketones with hydroxylamine.

In 1914, at the start of World War I, Knoevenagel was one of the first to enlist in the German army, where he saw active service and rose to the rank of staff officer. After the war, Knoevenagel resumed his academic work until his sudden death during an appendectomy.

The condensation of an aldehyde or ketone with an active methylene compound in the presence of a base is usually called a Knoevenagel reaction.[1] This method is a modification of the Perkin reaction[2] and has a similar mechanism. The base (either a primary or secondary amine) removes a proton from the active methylene group, which then reacts with the carbonyl compound. The following scheme is a general representation of the reaction.

147

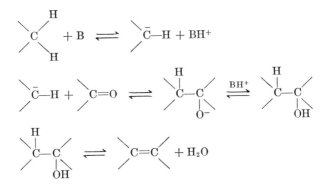

A variety of active methylene compounds and both aromatic and aliphatic aldehydes and ketones have been employed in the Knoevenagel reaction. According to Cope,[3] the best catalysts for the condensation of some aliphatic and cyclic ketones with cyanoacetic esters are ammonium and amine salts of organic acids. The use of acetamide as the catalyst in acetic acid solution was also shown to be very effective. By continuous removal of the water as it is formed in the reaction, good yields of the alkylidene cyanoacetic esters were obtained. The reaction may be illustrated as follows:

$$R_2CO + CH_2(CN)COOR' \longrightarrow R_2C=C(CN)COOR' + H_2O$$

Aromatic ketones can be condensed with ethyl cyanoacetate using ammonium acetate and acetic acid as the condensing agents.[4] For the condensation of aldehydes with ethyl cyanoacetate, the use of piperidine in alcohol proved to be more satisfactory than piperidine acetate or acetamide in acetic acid.[5]

Cragoe and associates[6] have shown that ammonium acetate (added portionwise) is a very effective catalyst in the reaction of diaryl ketones and certain hindered ketones with ethyl cyanoacetate. By this procedure the yield with benzophenone was 84%, which is substantially higher than was obtained previously.

The successful use of molar quantities of anhydrous KF in the reaction of aldehydes and ketones with diethyl malonate, ethyl cyanoacetate, and ethyl acetoacetate has been reported recently.[7] In refluxing alcohol, ethyl butylidenecyanoacetate was prepared in 40.9% yield. Condensation of paraformaldehyde with ethyl malonate in ether in the presence of KF for 4.5 hours at 20–25° yielded 61% of ethyl methylenemalonate along with a 20% yield of ethyl methylenedimalonate.

$$CH_2O + CH_2(CO_2Et)_2 \xrightarrow{\text{KF}} CH_2{=}C(CO_2Et)_2$$

A modification of the Knoevenagel condensation in which aryl aldehydes are condensed with malonic acid in the presence of pyridine and piperidine to give cinnamic acids is usually referred to as the *Doebner reaction*.[8]

References

1. E. Knoevenagel, *Ber. deut. Chem. Ges.* **29**, 172 (1896); *Ber. deut. Chem. Ges.* **31**, 730 (1898).
2. For a review of the Perkin and related reactions, see J. R. Johnson, *in* "Organic Reactions" (R. Adams, ed.), Vol. I, p. 210. Wiley, New York, 1942.
3. A. C. Cope, *J. Am. Chem. Soc.* **59**, 2327 (1937).
4. A. C. Cope, C. M. Hofmann, C. Wyckoff, and E. Hardenbergh, *J. Am. Chem. Soc.* **63**, 3452 (1941).
5. A. C. Cope and C. M. Hofmann, *J. Am. Chem. Soc.* **63**, 3456 (1941).
6. E. J. Cragoe, C. M. Robb, and J. M. Sprague, *J. Org. Chem.* **15**, 381 (1950).
7. H. Baba, H. Midorikawa, and S. Aoyama, *Chem. Abstr.* **53**, 15960 (1959); *J. Sci. Research Inst.* (*Tokyo*) **52**, 99 (1958) and accompanying papers.
8. O. Doebner, *Ber. deut. Chem. Ges.* **33**, 2140 (1900).

Knorr Pyrrole Synthesis

Ludwig Knorr (1859–1921) was born near Munich, Germany. He studied under Volhard, Emil Fischer, and Bunsen and assisted Fischer at Munich, Erlangen, and Würtzburg. In 1889, Knorr was appointed professor of chemistry at Jena. He carried out a considerable amount of research with nitrogen heterocyclic compounds and developed syntheses for pyrrole, pyrazole, and quinoline derivatives. He discovered the important pyrazolone drug, antipyrine. Knorr was also interested in keto-enol tautomerism.

A general and practical synthesis of pyrroles was introduced by Knorr in 1884.[1] It consists in the reaction of an α-amino ketone with a reactive methylene ketone.

$$
\begin{array}{c}
R'-C{\scriptstyle\nearrow}^{O} \\
R-C{\scriptstyle\diagdown}_{NH_2} \\
H
\end{array}
+
\begin{array}{c}
CH_2-R'' \\
CO-R'''
\end{array}
\longrightarrow
\begin{array}{c}
R'-C\!\!-\!\!-\!\!-\!\!C-R'' \\
R-C{\scriptstyle\diagdown}_{N}{\scriptstyle\diagup}C-R''' \\
H
\end{array}
$$

The condensation can be conveniently carried out starting with an isonitroso ketone. Reduction with zinc in glacial acetic acid gives the amino ketone, which need not be isolated. Excellent yields are obtained in this synthesis where R and R'' are acyl or carbalkoxy. If R'' is H, the main product is a pyrazine formed by self-condensation of the amino ketone.

$$
\begin{array}{c}
R'-C{\scriptstyle\nearrow}^{O} \\
R-C{\scriptstyle\diagdown}_{NH_2} \\
H
\end{array}
\begin{array}{c}
R \\
H_2N{\scriptstyle\diagdown}C-H \\
O{\scriptstyle\diagup}C-R'
\end{array}
\longrightarrow
\begin{array}{c}
R'-C{\scriptstyle\diagup}^{N}{\scriptstyle\diagdown}C-R \\
R-C{\scriptstyle\diagdown}_{N}{\scriptstyle\diagup}C-R'
\end{array}
$$

150

Knorr also showed that pyrroles are formed by the reaction of γ-diketones with ammonia or primary amines.[1] For example, diacetyl-succinic ester yields 3,4-dicarbethoxy-2,5-dimethylpyrrole.

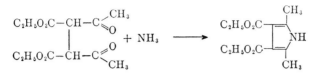

When the reaction was carried out in ether at 0°, the intermediate (I) was obtained.[2]

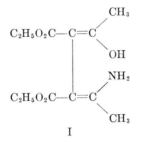

I

The Knorr synthesis[3] has been used in the preparation of pyrroles derived from porphyrins. In this connection, MacDonald[4] reported on the synthesis of pyrroles related to the uroporphyrins. The starting materials in this work were ethyl acetonedicarboxylate and benzyl aceto-acetate.

The use of dithionite ($Na_2S_2O_4$) as the reducing agent in the Knorr pyrrole synthesis has been recently reported.[5] Reduction of the isonitroso compounds may be carried out with this agent in aqueous solution at room temperature. Ethyl phenylazoacetate has also been employed in place of the isonitroso derivative.[5]

References

1. L. Knorr, *Ber. deut. Chem. Ges.* **17**, 1635 (1884); *Ann. Chem. Liebigs* **236**, 290 (1886).
2. L. Knorr and P. Rabe, *Ber. deut. Chem. Ges.* **33**, 3801 (1900).
3. A discussion of pyrrole ring closures is given by A. H. Corwin, *in* "Heterocyclic Compounds" (R. C. Elderfield, ed.), Vol. I, p. 287. Wiley, New York, 1950.
4. S. F. MacDonald, *Chem. & Ind. (London)* p. 759 (1951).
5. A. Treibs, R. Schmidt, and R. Zinsmeister, *Chem. Ber.* **90**, 79 (1957).

Kolbe-Schmitt Reaction

Adolph Wilhelm Hermann Kolbe (1818–1884) was born in Elliehausen near Göttingen, Germany. From 1838 to 1842 he was a student of Wöhler at the University of Göttingen. Later he worked in Bunsen's laboratory at Marburg, where in 1851 he was appointed successor to Bunsen in the professorial chair. In 1865, Kolbe became professor at the University of Leipzig.

With Wöhler, Kolbe investigated the reaction of chlorine with carbon disulfide which later led to his discovery of trichloroacetic acid and its transformation by means of potassium amalgam to acetic acid (1842). This was the second organic compound to be synthesized without the aid of living matter. Wöhler had synthesized urea in 1828.

Kolbe made many contributions to the field of organic chemistry. He determined the constitution of glycine, alanine, and lactic acid, prepared nitromethane from chloroacetic acid, and made an extensive study of the electrolysis of fatty acids. One of his greatest achievements was the preparation of salicylic acid from sodium phenoxide and carbon dioxide. He was also interested in the use of salicylic acid as an antiseptic.

The synthesis of phenolic carboxylic acids by heating an alkali phenolate with carbon dioxide is known as the Kolbe-Schmitt reaction.[1] In 1860[2] Kolbe discovered a method for the preparation of salicylic acid which involved heating sodium phenoxide with carbon dioxide under pressure at 180–200°.

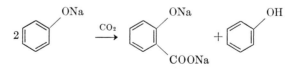

The method was improved by Schmitt,[3] (1885) who carried out the reaction at a lower temperature (125°) for a longer period of time. Under these conditions all the sodium phenolate was converted to salicylic acid. The introduction of the carboxylic acid group *ortho* to the hydroxy group usually proceeds in good yield. In some instances the *p*-hydroxy acid is obtained.[4]

A variety of phenolic compounds and conditions have been employed in the Kolbe-Schmitt reaction. β-Resorcylic acid is prepared by passing a rapid stream of carbon dioxide through a boiling aqueous solution of the potassium salt of resorcinol.[5]

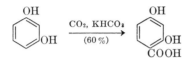

p-Aminosalicylic acid has been prepared in 80% yield from *m*-aminophenol[6] by autoclaving with Dry Ice and potassium bicarbonate solution.

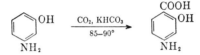

A new method of carboxylation of phenols was presented by Jones[7] based on the use of sodium ethyl (or methyl) carbonate, $NaOCO_2C_2H_5$. The addition of solid carbon dioxide to sodium ethylate precipitates sodium ethyl carbonate. When this is heated with phenol, ethyl alcohol distills. No autoclaving is necessary.

The *Marasse*[8] *modification* of the Kolbe-Schmitt reaction has been applied to approximately one hundred phenols.[9] The procedure involves heating a mixture of the phenol with an excess of anhydrous potassium carbonate at elevated temperatures (175°) under carbon dioxide pressure (1200–2000 psi) to give the potassium salt of the aromatic hydroxy acid. Potassium, rubidium or cesium carbonates may be used in this modification. The yields are good and in many cases are better than those obtained under the usual conditions of the Kolbe-Schmitt reaction.

References

1. A review of the Kolbe-Schmitt reaction is given by A. L. Lindsey and H. Jeskey, *Chem. Revs.* **57**, 583 (1957).
2. H. Kolbe, *Ann. Chem. Liebigs* **113**, 125 (1860).
3. R. Schmitt, *J. prakt. Chem.* **31**, 397 (1885).
4. See S. E. Hunt, J. Idris Jones, A. S. Lindsey, D. C. Killoh, and H. S. Turner, *J. Chem. Soc.* p. 3152 (1958) for a discussion of the influence of the alkali metal in the Kolbe-Schmitt reaction.
5. M. Nierenstein and D. A. Clibbens, *in* "Organic Syntheses" (A. H. Blatt, ed.), Coll. Vol. II, p. 557. Wiley, New York, 1943.
6. H. Erlenmeyer, B. Prijs, E. Sorkin, and E. Suter, *Helv. Chim. Acta* **31**, 988 (1948).
7. J. Idris Jones, *Chem. & Ind.* (*London*) p. 889 (1957).
8. S. Marasse, German Patent 73,279 (1893); P. Friedländer, "Fortschritte der Theerfarbenfabrikation," Vol. 3, p. 821 (1890–1894), Springer, Berlin (1896).
9. O. Baine, G. F. Adamson, J. W. Barton, J. L. Fitch, D. R. Swayampate, and H. Jeskey, *J. Org. Chem.* **19**, 510 (1954).

Kolbe's Electrochemical Reaction

A general and rather simple method for the preparation of hydrocarbons by the electrolysis of an alkali metal carboxylate was reported by Kolbe in 1849.[1] The reaction,[2] which is usually conducted in aqueous or methanolic solution, may be represented as follows, where R is an alkyl group usually containing six or more carbon atoms:

$$2RCO_2^- \longrightarrow R \cdot R + 2CO_2 + 2e$$

The reaction has been extended and is now a valuable method for the preparation of many organic compounds. Monoesters of dicarboxylic acids have been employed in the reaction.[3] By using a mixture of a monocarboxylic acid and a half-ester of a dicarboxylic acid,[4] both symmetrical and unsymmetrical products have been obtained. For example, the electrolysis of methyl hydrogen adipate with acetic acid gave hexanoic acid (obtained after hydrolysis of the ester) as well as the expected symmetrical products.

$$CH_3OOC(CH_2)_4COOH + CH_3COOH \longrightarrow CH_3(CH_2)_4COOH$$

By increasing the ratio of monocarboxylic acid to half-ester, a greater conversion to the unsymmetrical product resulted.

Similar results were obtained with mixtures of keto acids.[5] The products from the electrolysis of the keto acids (I and II) were the diketones (III, IV, and V).

$$\begin{cases} \text{I} & CH_3CO(CH_2)_4COOH \\ \text{II} & CH_3CO(CH_2)_8COOH \end{cases} \longrightarrow \begin{cases} CH_3CO(CH_2)_4(CH_2)_4COCH_3 & \text{III} \\ CH_3CO(CH_2)_4(CH_2)_8COCH_3 & \text{IV} \\ CH_3CO(CH_2)_8(CH_2)_8COCH_3) & \text{V} \end{cases}$$

The use of benzyl esters of dibasic acid esters in the Kolbe electrochemical reaction has been reported.[6]

155

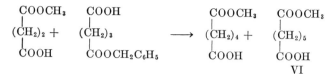

$$
\begin{array}{ccc}
\underset{\overset{|}{\text{COOH}}}{\overset{\text{COOCH}_3}{|}}(\text{CH}_2)_2 + & \underset{\overset{|}{\text{COOCH}_2\text{C}_6\text{H}_5}}{\overset{\text{COOH}}{|}}(\text{CH}_2)_3 & \longrightarrow & \underset{\overset{|}{\text{COOH}}}{\overset{\text{COOCH}_3}{|}}(\text{CH}_2)_4 + & \underset{\overset{|}{\text{COOH}}}{\overset{\text{COOCH}_3}{|}}(\text{CH}_2)_5
\end{array}
$$
VI

The unsymmetrical product VI was obtained after catalytic debenzylation with palladium-on-strontium carbonate. A small amount of suberic acid was also obtained after debenzylation.

Lindsey and Peterson[7] have electrolyzed carboxylic acids and dicarboxylic acid derivatives in the presence of dienes such as 1,3-butadiene. They obtained a variety of products including olefins, dienes, and esters of unsaturated dicarboxylic acids.

References

1. H. Kolbe, *Ann. Chem. Liebigs* **69**, 257 (1849).
2. A review of the reaction is given by B. C. L. Weedon, *Quart. Revs.* (*London*) **6**, 380 (1952); see also, B. C. L. Weedon, *in* "Advances in Organic Chemistry" (R. A. Raphael, E. C. Taylor, and H. Wynberg, eds.), Vol. 1, pp. 1–34. Interscience, New York, 1960.
3. The electrochemical reaction as applied to monoesters of dicarboxylic acids is referred to as the *Crum-Brown-Walker reaction*. A. Crum-Brown and G. Walker, *Ann. Chem. Liebigs* **274**, 71 (1893).
4. W. S. Greaves, R. P. Linstead, B. R. Shephard, S. L. S. Thomas, and B. C. L. Weedon, *J. Chem. Soc.* p. 3326 (1950); R. P. Linstead, J. C. Lunt, and B. C. L. Weeden, *J. Chem. Soc.* pp. 3331, 3333.
5. M. Stoll, *Helv. Chim. Acta* **34**, 1817 (1951).
6. L. Dolejs and L. Novotny, *Collection Czechoslov. Chem. Communs.* **19**, 716 (1954).
7. R. V. Lindsey, Jr., and M. L. Peterson, *J. Am. Chem. Soc.* **81**, 2073 (1959).

Leuckart Reaction

Carl Louis Rudolf Alexander Leuckart (1854–1889) was born in Giessen, Germany, the son of a zoology professor. At Heidelberg he studied physics under Kirchhoff and chemistry under Bunsen. From there he went to Leipzig, where he worked under the direction of Kolbe and received his doctor's degree in 1879. Leuckart continued his training at Munich under von Baeyer and after three years left for Göttingen, where he became an assistant professor. His promising career in chemistry was ended by his sudden death as a result of a fall in his parent's home.

Leuckart's contributions include an investigation of urea and its derivatives; the preparation of thiophenols and their ethers from diazonium compounds and xanthates[1] (Leuckart thiopenol reaction); and his reductive alkylation procedure.

The conversion of aldehydes and ketones to the corresponding amines by heating with formamide, ammonium formate, or formamide and formic acid is generally called the Leuckart reaction.[2,3]

$$RR'CO + 2HCOONH_4 \longrightarrow RR'CHNHCHO + NH_3 + CO_2 + 2H_2O$$

$$RR'CHNHCHO \xrightarrow{H_2O} RR'CHNH_2 + HCOOH$$

According to Crossley and Moore,[4] a mixture of formamide and formic acid gives the best yields in the Leuckart reaction. Aromatic aldehydes and high-boiling ketones are best suited for this reaction. By employing substituted formamides or formates derived from primary or secondary amines, secondary or tertiary amines can be prepared via the Leuckart reaction.

The reaction has been applied in the preparation of some γ-aryl-propylamines for pharmacodynamic and chemotherapeutic studies.[5] An illustration is the synthesis of 1,3,3-triphenylpropylamine from β,β-diphenylpropiophenone.

$$(C_6H_5)_2CHCH_2COC_6H_5 \longrightarrow (C_6H_5)_2CHCH_2CH(NH_2)C_6H_5$$

157

In the reaction of ketones with dialkylformamides, magnesium chloride catalysis is necessary.[6] For example, with magnesium chloride, cyclohexanone and N-formylpiperidine gave N-cyclohexylpiperidine (I). In the absence of the catalyst the product was not obtained. The same tertiary amine (I) was prepared by Smith and Macdonald[7] by refluxing cyclohexanone and piperidine formate.

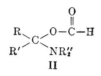

These authors have considered the formate esters of carbinol amines (II) as intermediates which might rearrange to a tertiary amine by a 1,3-hydride shift.

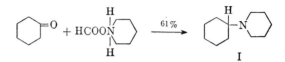

An investigation of the mechanism of the Leuckart reaction was reported by Pollard and Young.[8] On the basis of kinetic studies involving the first step in the reaction and spectrophotometric investigation of intermediate products, the following mechanism was proposed:

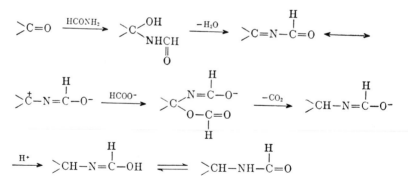

The initial step involves the addition of formamide to the carbonyl group. At elevated temperatures water is split out to give an intermediate which has a conjugated system. The water then hydrolyzes

158

some formamide to give ammonium formate, which can act as the reducing agent. A hydride-ion shift with release of carbon dioxide followed by addition of a proton from the ammonium ion gives the formyl derivative of the primary amine.

No explanation is given for the preparation of secondary or tertiary amines prepared via the Leuckart reaction.[9]

Eschweiler-Clarke reaction.[10] This reaction is closely related to the Leuckart reaction. It appears to be specific for the preparation of N-methyl compounds by the reaction of a primary or secondary amine with formaldehyde and formic acid. The yields of tertiary amines prepared by this method are usually very satisfactory.

$$RNH_2 \longrightarrow RN(CH_3)_2$$

$$R_2NH \longrightarrow R_2NCH_3$$

The reaction is usually carried out by heating a mixture of the amine (1 mole), 35–40% formaldehyde (2.2 moles), and formic acid (5 moles) on a steam bath until no further evidence of carbon dioxide evolution is observed. Prolonged heating appears to have no adverse effect. The tertiary amine can be isolated from the reaction mixture by adding an excess of base and extracting with an organic solvent.

References

1. R. Leuckart, *J. prakt. Chem.* **41**, 179 (1890).
2. A review of the Leuckart reaction is given by M. L. Moore, *in* "Organic Reactions" (R. Adams, ed.), Vol. V, p. 301. Wiley, New York, 1949.
3. R. Leuckart, *Ber. deut. Chem. Ges.* **18**, 2341 (1885).
4. F. S. Crossley and M. L. Moore, *J. Org. Chem.* **9**, 529 (1944).
5. J. H. Burckhalter and S. H. Johnson, *J. Am. Chem. Soc.* **73**, 4830 (1951).
6. J. F. Bunnett and J. L. Marks, *J. Am. Chem. Soc.* **71**, 1587 (1949).
7. P. A. S. Smith and A. J. Macdonald, *J. Am. Chem. Soc.* **72**, 1037 (1950).
8. C. B. Pollard and D. C. Young, *J. Org. Chem.* **16**, 661 (1951).
9. For a discussion of the mechanism of the Leuckart-Wallach reaction, see V. Franzen, *Chem. Ztg.* **80**, 779 (1956).
10. W. Eschweiler, *Ber. deut. Chem. Ges.* **38**, 880 (1905); H. T. Clarke, H. B. Gillespie, and S. Z. Weisshaus, *J. Am. Chem. Soc.* **55**, 4571 (1933).

Lossen Rearrangement

Wilhelm Clemens Lossen (1838–1906) was born in Kreuznach, Germany. He obtained his Ph.D. degree in 1862 at Göttingen and served as an assistant there. He also served as an assistant at Karlsruhe, Halle, and Heidelberg, where later he became professor of chemistry. In 1877, Lossen left for Königsberg to assume a similar position. His interests centered on hydroxylamines, their preparation, properties, and derivatives.

The Lossen rearrangement usually refers to the decomposition of hydroxamic acids or their derivatives to yield isocyanates.[1,2]

$$\text{HONHCOR} \longrightarrow \text{RNCO} + \text{H}_2\text{O}$$

Monohydroxamic acids are generally prepared by the reaction of an ester with hydroxylamine in the presence of sodium alkoxide.

$$\text{RCOOR}' + \text{NH}_2\text{OH} \xrightarrow{\text{NaOC}_2\text{H}_5} \underset{\overset{\|}{\text{O}}}{\text{RC}}\text{—NHOH} \rightleftharpoons \underset{\overset{|}{\text{OH}}}{\text{RC}}\text{=NOH}$$

Potassium hydroxide has been used in the synthesis of benzohydroxamic acid.[3] The rearrangement may be produced by heating alone or with a dehydrating agent such as thionyl chloride, acetic anhydride, or phosphorus pentoxide. The use of polyphosphoric acid in the Lossen rearrangement has been reported by Snyder et al.[4] Aromatic acids can be converted to the amines in a matter of minutes by heating (150–170°) with hydroxylamine and polyphosphoric acid. Amines are also obtained by heating hydroxamic acids with this reagent.

A classical example of the use of the Lossen rearrangement is in the conversion of camphor to epicamphor.[5]

The methyl ester of bornylene-3-carboxylic acid, prepared from camphor, on treatment with hydroxylamine gave the hydroxamic acid. Formation of the isocyanate and hydrolysis to the ketone may be illustrated as follows:

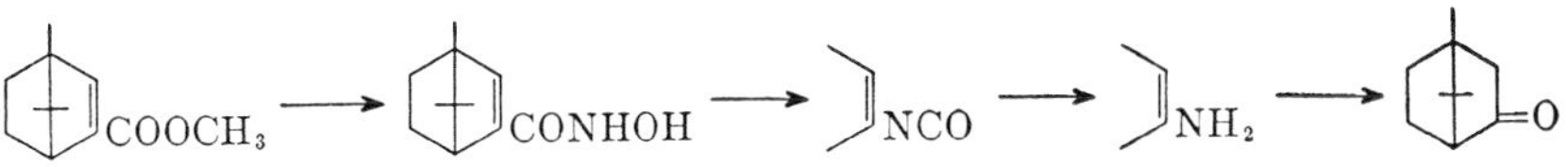

The rearrangement of monohydroxamic acid derivatives of dibasic acids may give rise to polymeric amides.[6] For example, when the sodium salt of benzoyl 5-carboxyvalerohydroxamate is heated in toluene, a polymer is obtained.

$$\text{HOOC(CH}_2)_4\text{CON—OCOC}_6\text{H}_5 \longrightarrow [\text{—OC(CH}_2)_4\text{NH—}]_n$$

with Na on the nitrogen.

If the rearrrangement is carried out in water, the product is an urea derivative, $[\text{HOOC(CH}_2)_4\text{NH}]_2\text{CO}$.

Aliphatic dihydroxamic acids are converted to diisocyanates by heating in benzene or toluene in the presence of thionyl chloride or phosgene.[7] An example is the formation of octamethylene diisocyanate from sebacic dihydroxamic acid.

The Lossen rearrangement is similar to the Hofmann and Curtius rearrangements and offers an additional method for converting a carboxylic acid to an amine. Retention of configuration of the migrating group is shown in the preparation of (—)-α-phenylethylamine from benzoyl phenylmethylacetohydroxamate.[8]

$$\text{RCH(CH}_3)\text{COOH} \longrightarrow \text{RCH(CH}_3)\text{COCl} \xrightarrow{\text{NH}_2\text{OH}} \text{RCH(CH}_3)\text{CONHOH}$$

$$\xrightarrow{\text{RCOCl}} \text{RCH(CH}_3)\text{C(OH)=NOCOR} \xrightarrow[\text{CH}_3\text{OH}]{K} \text{RCH(CH}_3)\text{CON—OCOR}$$

with K on the nitrogen.

$$\longrightarrow \text{RCH(CH}_3)\text{NCO} \xrightarrow{\text{HCl}} \text{RCH(CH}_3)\text{NH}_2 \qquad R = C_6H_5$$

Bauer and Miarka[9] have shown that the Lossen rearrangement of several cis-N-phenylsulfonyloxy-1,2-cyclohexanedicarboximides was stereospecific giving cis-2-aminocyclohexanecarboxylic acids.

161

References

1. W. Lossen, *Ann. Chem. Liebigs* **161,** 347 (1872).
2. H. L. Yale, *Chem. Revs.* **33,** 209 (1943).
3. C. R. Hauser and W. B. Renfrow, *in* "Organic Syntheses" (A. H. Blatt, ed.), Coll. Vol. II, p. 67. Wiley, New York, 1943.
4. H. R. Snyder, C. T. Elston, and D. B. Kellom, *J. Am. Chem. Soc.* **75,** 2014 (1953).
5. J. Bredt and W. H. Perkin, Jr., *J. prakt. Chem.* **89,** 209 (1914).
6. C. D. Hurd, C. M. Buess, and L. Bauer, *J. Org. Chem.* **17,** 865 (1952).
7. J. B. Dickey, J. M. Straley, and T. E. Stavin, U. S. Patent 2,394,597 (Feb. 12, 1946); *Chem. Abstr.* **40,** 2848 (1946).
8. A. Campbell and J. Kenyon, *J. Chem. Soc.* p. 25 (1946).
9. L. Bauer and S. V. Miarka, *J. Org. Chem.* **24,** 1293 (1959).

McFadyen-Stevens Reduction

J. S. McFadyen (1908–   ) was born in Toronto, Canada. He studied under T. S. Stevens at the University of Glasgow and received his Ph.D. degree in 1936. After working for fifteen years with the Imperial Chemical Industries' dyestuffs division in England, McFadyen returned to Canada, where he is now technical assistant to the chemistry department of the Canadian Industries Limited, Montreal.

*   *   *

Thomas S. Stevens (1900–   ) was born in Renfrew, Scotland. He studied at the University of Glasgow and then under W. H. Perkin at Oxford University, where he received his doctorate degree. At present, Stevens is a reader in organic chemistry at the University of Sheffield.

Some of Stevens' interests in chemistry include alkaloids and reaction mechanisms, especially of molecular rearrangements.

In 1936, McFadyen and Stevens[1] introduced a new method for converting an aromatic carboxylic acid to the corresponding aldehyde. The procedure is illustrated by the preparation of benzaldehyde from ethyl benzoate. The benzenesulfonhydrazide formed from the

$$C_6H_5COOC_2H_5 \xrightarrow{NH_2NH_2} C_6H_5CONHNH_2 \xrightarrow{C_6H_5SO_2Cl}$$

$$C_6H_5CONHNHSO_2C_6H_5 \xrightarrow{Na_2CO_3} C_6H_5CHO + C_6H_5SO_2Na + N_2$$

hydrazide with benzenesulfonyl chloride is dissolved in ethylene glycol, heated to 150–165°, and anhydrous sodium or potassium carbonate is added. Nitrogen is evolved. After about one minute hot water is added to the reaction mixture. The aldehyde may be extracted with a suitable organic solvent or isolated by steam distillation. The yields of aromatic aldehydes are generally good.[2]

163

The reaction is also applicable to the preparation of heterocyclic aldehydes. For example, 2- and 3-pyridinealdehydes[3] and the 3-, 5-, 6-, and 8-quinolinealdehydes[4] have been prepared by the McFadyen-Stevens reduction. The yields (13–45%) in the heterocyclic series are lower than those obtained for the aromatic aldehydes.

Roberts[5] has shown that cyclopropanecarboxylic benzenesulfon-hydrazide can be converted to cyclopropanecarboxaldehyde in 16% yield by the McFadyen-Stevens reduction.

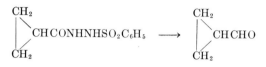

References

1. J. S. McFadyen and T. S. Stevens, *J. Chem. Soc.* p. 584 (1936).
2. The McFadyen-Stevens procedure is included in a review of useful reactions for converting carboxylic acids into aldehydes. E. Mossetig *in* "Organic Reactions" (R. Adams, ed.), Vol. VIII, p. 218. Wiley, New York, 1954.
3. C. Niemann, R. N. Lewis, and J. T. Hays, *J. Am. Chem. Soc.* **64,** 1678 (1942); C. Niemann and J. T. Hays, *J. Am. Chem. Soc.* **65,** 482 (1943).
4. A. H. Cook, I. M. Heilbron, and L. Steger, *J. Chem. Soc.* p. 413 (1943).
5. J. D. Roberts, *J. Am. Chem. Soc.* **73,** 2959 (1951).

Mannich Reaction

Carl Ulrich Franz Mannich (1877–1947) was born in Breslau, Germany. He was a student at the Universities of Marburg, Berlin, and Basel. He was awarded the doctor's degree at Basel in 1903. After serving on the faculties of Göttingen and Frankfurt, he was appointed professor and head of the Pharmacy Institute at Berlin in 1927.

Mannich was particularly interested in the synthesis of organic compounds for pharmacological use. He isolated crystalline cardiac glycosides from the Strophanthus and Digitalis plants. From 1917 over a period of about thirty years Mannich carried out an extensive investigation of the applicability and scope of the reaction which bears his name. He found that the reaction of methylamine with formaldehyde and acetone gave a piperidine derivative from which he prepared methyl arecoline. Mannich synthesized a large number of amino ketones and converted them to amino alcohols. He used these for the preparations of esters of p-aminobenzoic acid to be tested as local anesthetics.

The condensation of a compound containing one or more active hydrogen atoms with formaldehyde and ammonia or a primary or secondary amine which results in the replacement of the hydrogen by an aminomethyl group is known as the Mannich reaction. An illustration is the preparation of 4-diethylamino-2-butanone hydrochloride from the reaction of acetone with formaldehyde and diethylamine hydrochloride.

$$CH_3COCH_3 + CH_2O + (C_2H_5)_2NH \cdot HCl \longrightarrow CH_3COCH_2CH_2N(C_2H_5)_2 \cdot HCl$$

In this instance, there are additional active hydrogen atoms present and more than one diethylaminomethyl group may be introduced.

Although isolated examples of this type of reaction preceded Mannich's work,[1] he was the first to recognize its general application in organic syntheses. A large variety of compounds[2] including ketones, aldehydes, esters, and phenols have been successfully employed in the Mannich reaction. The type of amine taking part in the reaction has also varied widely.

The preparation of Mannich bases of phenolic compounds may be illustrated with 5-chloro-8-hydroxyquinoline.[3] Condensation with diethylamine and paraformaldehyde results in the formation of 5-chloro-7-diethylaminomethyl-8-quinolinol, an amebicidal agent.

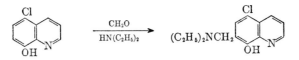

Traces of iron have a profound effect on the Mannich reaction between terminal acetylenes, formaldehyde, and diethylamine.[4] Yields up to 80% were obtained in the presence of ferric chloride where otherwise practically no reaction occurred.

$$-C\equiv CH + CH_2O + NH(C_2H_5)_2 \longrightarrow -C\equiv C-CH_2N(C_2H_5)_2$$

The Mannich base, 4-diethylamino-2-butanone, may be converted to methyl vinyl ketone by steam distillation. The yields are usually poor, however, because of polymerization. Robinson[5] showed that the methiodide of this base could be employed as a gradual source of methyl vinyl ketone in the synthesis of cyclic ketones.

$$CH_3COCH_2CH_2\overset{\overset{\displaystyle I}{|}}{N}(C_2H_5)_2 \longrightarrow CH_3COCH=CH_2 + \underset{\underset{\displaystyle CH_3}{|}}{N}(C_2H_5)_2 \cdot HI$$
$$\underset{\displaystyle CH_3}{|}$$

The quaternary salt of the piperidino Mannich base has been found to be a superior reagent for this purpose.[6]

Essentially, the quaternary salt behaves as an alkylating agent; the tertiary amine is eliminated, and a carbon-to-carbon linkage is effected. The vinyl ketone may be pictured as undergoing a Michael condensation. This type of reaction has been employed in the synthesis of the

166

amino acid, tryptophan,[7] which involves the alkylation of ethyl acetamidomalonate with gramine methiodide.

Phenolic Mannich base methiodides and oxides have been shown to react readily in basic media with a variety of nucleophiles.[8] For example, with methoxide ion the corresponding benzyl methyl ethers are obtained.

The use of a Mannich base itself as the alkylating agent has been reported by Dodson and Sollmann.[9] 6-Dimethylamino-4-ketocaproic acid, the Mannich base from levulinic acid, was condensed with ethyl malonate, and the resulting product was hydrolyzed and then decarboxylated to γ-ketosuberic acid.

$$CH_3CO(CH_2)_2COOH \longrightarrow (CH_3)_2NCH_2CH_2CO(CH_2)_2COOH \xrightarrow{CH_2(COOC_2H_5)_2}$$

$$(C_2H_5OOC)_2CH(CH_2)_2CO(CH_2)_2COOH \xrightarrow[-CO_2]{HOH} HOOC(CH_2)_3CO(CH_2)_2COOH$$

The mechanism of the Mannich reaction has not been established. The aminomethanol formed from the amine and formaldehyde may be an intermediate in the reaction.[10,11]

$$CH_2O + HN(CH_3)_2 \rightleftharpoons N(CH_3)_2CH_2OH$$

Methylene-bisamines have also been suggested as intermediates.[12] These compounds, which can be formed under the conditions of the Mannich reaction, react with active methylene compounds to yield Mannich bases.

References

1. C. Mannich and W. Krösche, *Arch. Pharm.* **250**, 647 (1912).
2. A review of the Mannich reaction is given by F. F. Blicke, *in* "Organic Reactions" (R. Adams, ed.), Vol. I, p. 303. Wiley, New York, 1942; K. W. Merz, *Pharmazie* **11**, 505 (1956).
3. J. H. Burckhalter and S. H. Johnson, *J. Am. Chem. Soc.* **73**, 4837 (1951).
4. I. N. Nazarov and E. A. Mistryukov, *Chem. Abstr.* **52**, 12751 (1958).
5. E. C. du Feu, F. J. McQuillin, and R. Robinson, *J. Chem. Soc.* p. 53 (1937).
6. A. L. Wilds and R. G. Werth, *J. Org. Chem.* **17**, 1149 (1952).

7. H. R. Snyder and C. W. Smith, *J. Am. Chem. Soc.* **66**, 350 (1944); N. F. Albertson, S. Archer, and C. M. Suter, *J. Am. Chem. Soc.* **66**, 500 (1944).
8. P. D. Gardner, H. S. Rafsanjani, and L. Rand, *J. Am. Chem. Soc.* **81**, 3364 (1959); see also for references to this type of reaction.
9. R. M. Dodson and P. Sollmann, *J. Am. Chem. Soc.* **73**, 4197 (1951).
10. E. R. Alexander and E. J. Underhill, *J. Am. Chem. Soc.* **71**, 4014 (1949).
11. Evidence for this type of intermediate was shown by E. Hope and R. Robinson, *J. Chem. Soc.* **99**, 2114 (1911); **103**, 361 (1913), in the reaction of cotarnine with acetophenone.
12. S. V. Lieberman and E. C. Wagner, *J. Org. Chem.* **14**, 1001 (1949).

Meerwein Condensation

Hans L. Meerwein (1879–   ) was born in Hamburg, Germany. He studied at Wiesbaden, Bonn, and Charlottenburg. In 1903, Meerwein was awarded his doctor's degree at Bonn, where, in 1914, he became associate professor. Eight years later he was appointed professor and director of the Chemical Institute at Königsberg and since 1929 has held a similar position at Marburg.

Meerwein has made many notable contributions in organic chemistry. These include the Meerwein reaction, the reduction of aldehydes and ketones with aluminum alcoholates, and an investigation of the pinacol-pinacolone rearrangement and reactions with diazomethane.

The reaction of an aromatic diazonium chloride or bromide with an α,β-unsaturated carbonyl compound which results in the attachment of the aromatic nucleus at the α or β position is known as the Meerwein condensation.[1,2] The carbonyl compounds employed by Meerwein in this reaction yielded α-aryl derivatives. For example, the reaction of cinnamic acid with p-nitrobenzenediazonium chloride gave p-nitrostilbene. In this case the reaction is accompanied by decarboxylation.

$$NO_2C_6H_4N_2Cl + C_6H_5CH{=}CHCOOH \longrightarrow$$

$$NO_2C_6H_4CH{=}CHC_6H_5 + CO_2 + N_2 + HCl$$

Koelsch[3] showed that coupling could occur at the β position. With acrylonitrile or methyl acrylate, cinnamic acid derivatives were obtained. The initial product in the reaction of an aryl diazonium chloride with acrylonitrile is the α-chloro-β-arylpropionitrile. Treatment of this intermediate with diethylaniline or potassium hydroxide yields the β-arylacrylonitrile.

169

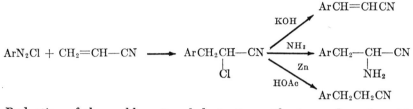

Reduction of the α-chloro-β-aryl derivative with zinc and acetic acid gives the β-arylpropionitrile; treatment with ammonium hydroxide leads to formation of an α-aminopropionitrile.[2]

The mechanism of the Meerwein reaction has been explained by both a radical reaction[2,4] and an ionic process.[1,5] More recently, Dickerman[6] has investigated the mechanism of the Meerwein reaction conducted in acetone solution. The catalyst in the reaction appears to be cuprous chloride which is formed from cupric chloride and acetone. The results of kinetic studies have been interpreted in terms of a radical mechanism.

References

1. H. Meerwein, E. Buchner, and K. van Emster, *J. prakt. Chem.* **152**, 237 (1939).
2. A discussion of the Meerwein condensation is given by E. Müller, *Angew. Chem.* **61**, 179 (1949).
3. C. F. Koelsch, *J. Am. Chem. Soc.* **65**, 57 (1943).
4. C. F. Koelsch and V. C. Boekelheide, *J. Am. Chem. Soc.* **66**, 412 (1944).
5. F. Bergmann and D. Schapiro, *J. Org. Chem.* **12**, 57 (1947); see also W. A. Cowdrey and D. S. Davies, *Quart. Revs. (London)* **6**, 365, 377 (1952).
6. S. C. Dickerman, K. Weiss, and A. K. Ingberman, *J. Am. Chem. Soc.* **80**, 1904 (1958).

Meerwein-Ponndorf-Verley Reduction

The selective reduction of a carbonyl compound to an alcohol in the presence of aluminum alkoxides is commonly referred to as the Meerwein-Ponndorf-Verley reduction.[1,2] The conversion, which is reversible,[3] is represented by the general equation:

$$RR'CO + R''_2CHOH \rightleftharpoons RR'CHOH + R''_2CO$$

Aliphatic and aromatic aldehydes and ketones have been reduced satisfactorily by this method. Ordinarily the procedure involves refluxing the carbonyl compound in isopropyl alcohol in the presence of aluminum isopropoxide. The acetone formed by oxidation according to the above equation ($R'' = CH_3$) is removed continuously by slow distillation to force the reaction to completion. Aldehydes are in general more rapidly reduced than ketones. Other groups, such as nitro or carboxylic esters, carbon-carbon double bonds, and most reactive halogens are not affected by aluminum isopropoxide.[4]

With aldehydes and reactive ketones the slow addition of the carbonyl compound to the reaction mixture has been suggested[5] as a method of improving the yield of the desired alcohol. It has been shown[6] that in a majority of cases removal of acetone is unnecessary. Good yields of reduced products are obtained by simply refluxing the isopropyl alcohol solution containing the carbonyl compound and aluminum isopropoxide for a short time. By this modified method benzhydrol was obtained from benzophenone in 98% yield.

$$C_6H_5COC_6H_5 \longrightarrow C_6H_5CHOHC_6H_5$$

Jackman and Mills[5] have proposed the following mechanism for the Meerwein-Ponndorf-Verley reduction which in some respects is similar to that suggested in the Cannizzaro reaction (p. 41). The carbonyl compound coordinates with the aluminum atom in aluminum

171

isopropoxide to give the complex (I), which can be written as a six-membered cyclic structure (II).

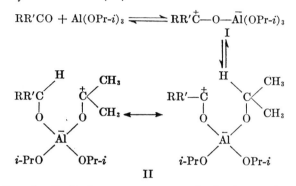

$$RR'CO + Al(OPr\text{-}i)_3 \rightleftharpoons RR'\overset{+}{C}\text{—}O\text{—}\overset{-}{Al}(OPr\text{-}i)_3$$
$$I$$

II

The transfer of a hydride ion[7] is apparently facilitated by this cyclic state. Decomposition of the cyclic intermediate with acid gives the reduced product RR'CHOH. In the presence of isopropyl alcohol an exchange reaction occurs with (II) regenerating the aluminum isopropoxide. The reduction, however, can be performed in the absence of isopropyl alcohol.

References

1. H. Meerwein and R. Schmidt, *Ann. Chem. Liebigs* **444**, 221 (1925); W. Ponndorf, *Angew. Chem.* **39**, 138 (1926); A. Verley, *Bull. soc. chim. Paris* **37**, 537, 871 (1925).
2. A review of the reaction is given by A. L. Wilds, *in* "Organic Reactions" (R. Adams, ed.), Vol. II, p. 178. Wiley, New York, 1944.
3. The reverse reaction is the Oppenauer oxidation. See p. 177.
4. For a recent discussion of the Meerwein-Ponndorf-Verley reduction, see W. A. Johnson and G. E. H. Skrimshire, *Chem. & Ind. (London)* p. 380 (1951).
5. L. M. Jackman and J. A. Mills, *Nature* **164**, 789 (1949).
6. W. L. Truett and W. N. Moulton, *J. Am. Chem. Soc.* **73**, 5913 (1951).
7. A discussion of hydride transfer reactions is given by N. C. Deno, H. J. Peterson, and G. S. Saines, *Chem. Revs.* **60**, 7 (1960).

Michael Reaction

Arthur Michael (1853–1942) was born in Buffalo, New York. His father moved to England for business reasons and the family joined him there. Michael studied at Heidelberg, where he became an assistant to Bunsen. There he became a friend of Gabriel, with whom he went to Berlin to work under Hofmann. From there, Michael went to Paris to work with Wurtz and then to Russia to be with Mendelejeff. Upon his return to the United States he taught at Tufts College, where he also carried out some of his research. In 1909, Michael became the director of the chemical laboratory at the new Clark University and shortly afterwards was appointed professor of chemistry at Harvard. A considerable amount of Michael's work was done in his own laboratory at Newton Center, Massachusetts. His reputation as a chemist attracted many graduate students from Germany.

Michael worked on a large variety of subjects. His extensive work on the reactions of activated methylene compounds is well known. In his later years he was concerned with problems in physical chemistry.

The addition of active methylene compounds to α,β-unsaturated compounds in the presence of a basic catalyst such as sodium ethoxide or piperidine is referred to as the Michael reaction.[1] An illustration is the condensation of the ethyl acetoacetate with acrylonitrile.

$$CH_3COCH_2COOC_2H_5 + CH_2{=}CHCN \longrightarrow CH_3CO\underset{\underset{\displaystyle CH_2CH_2CN}{|}}{CH}{-}COOC_2H_5$$

With sodium ethoxide as the catalyst the reaction may be carried out by allowing a solution of the reactants, in a suitable solvent, to stand at room temperature for two or more days. A minimum amount of catalyst is used to prevent a reversal of the reaction. The use of piperidine usually requires higher reaction temperature.[2]

The Michael reaction is commonly represented as follows:

$$
\begin{array}{ccc}
\overset{\text{R}'}{\underset{\text{R}-\text{CH}-\text{C}-\text{R}''}{\diagdown}}\overset{\text{O}}{\diagup}
& \xrightarrow{\text{B}} &
\overset{\text{R}'}{\underset{\text{R}-\underset{\ominus}{\text{C}}-\text{C}-\text{R}''}{\diagdown}}\overset{\text{O}}{\diagup} + \text{BH}
\end{array}
$$

$$
\overset{\text{R}'}{\underset{\text{R}-\underset{\ominus}{\text{C}}-\text{C}-\text{R}''}{\diagdown}}\overset{\text{O}}{\diagup} + \text{CH}_2{=}\text{CH}{-}\text{C}{\equiv}\text{N} \longrightarrow
\overset{\text{R}'}{\underset{\underset{\text{R}''-\text{C}=\text{O}}{|}}{\text{R}-\text{C}-\text{CH}_2-\underset{\ominus}{\text{CH}}-\text{C}{\equiv}\text{N}}}
$$

Removal of a proton from the activated methylene group gives an anion which reacts with the α,β-unsaturated compound to form a new anion. The latter may pick up a proton from the conjugated base or from the activated methylene group.

Among the numerous methylene compounds used in the Michael reaction are ethyl malonate, ethyl cyanoacetate, ethyl acetoacetate, and benzyl cyanide. Compounds with activated double bonds (acceptors) include α,β-unsaturated aldehydes, ketones, esters, and nitriles.

Internal Michael reactions have been reported with some *ortho*-substituted cinnamic esters (I), where Z is O, S, or NCH₃.[3]

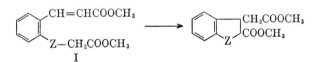

$$\text{I}$$

The use of nitro compounds in the Michael reaction is illustrated by the condensation of potassium dinitromethane with two moles of acrylonitrile.[4]

$$\text{O}_2\text{N}-\text{CH}{=}\text{NO}_2\text{K} + 2\text{CH}_2{=}\text{CHCN} \longrightarrow (\text{NCCH}_2\text{CH}_2)_2\text{C}(\text{NO}_2)_2$$

An interesting application of the Michael addition is involved in the *Stork reaction.*[5]

References

1. A. Michael, *J. prakt. Chem.* **35**, 349 (1887).
2. A comprehensive review of the Michael reaction is given by E. D. Bergmann, D. Ginsburg, and R. Pappo, *in* "Organic Reactions" (R. Adams, ed.), Vol. X, p. 179. Wiley, New York, 1959.
3. C. F. Koelsch and C. R. Stephens, *J. Am. Chem. Soc.* **72**, 2209 (1950).
4. L. Herzog, M. H. Gold, and R. D. Geckler, *J. Am. Chem. Soc.* **73**, 749 (1951).
5. See page 231.

Nef Reaction

John Ulric Nef (1862–1915) was born in Herisau, Switzerland. At the age of sixteen he came to America, where in 1880 he entered Harvard University. He was awarded a fellowship which enabled him to study under von Baeyer at Munich. Nef received the doctor's degree in 1886 and returned to the United States to become professor of chemistry at Purdue. After two years he went to Clark University. In 1892, he left to take the professorial chair at the University of Chicago, where he spent his remaining years.

Nef's interest in the phenomena of tautomerism, which began at Munich, led to his investigations of tautomeric compounds, especially of the keto-enol type and of the nitroparaffin salts. He suggested that the metal in these salts was attached to oxygen and not to carbon, as had been proposed by Victor Meyer. Nef spent considerable time investigating the chemistry of bivalent carbon with the purpose of obtaining methylene.

The Nef reaction consists in the formation of aldehydes or ketones by the addition of sodium salts of primary or secondary nitroparaffins to an excess of cold mineral acid.[1,2]

$$2RCH{=}N({\rightarrow}O)ONa + 2H^+ \longrightarrow 2RCHO + 2Na^+ + N_2O + H_2O$$
$$2RR'C{=}N({\rightarrow}O)ONa + 2H^+ \longrightarrow 2RR'CO + 2Na^+ + N_2O + H_2O$$

Examples of the Nef reaction are the conversion of 2-nitropropane to acetone in 85% yield[3] and the preparation of several 6-phenyl-3-cyclohexen-1-ones from the corresponding 4-nitro-5-phenylcyclohexenes.[4]

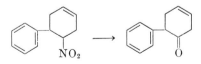

An excellent article on the mechanism of the Nef reaction was presented by van Tamelen and Thiede,[5] which indicates that the mechanism is similar to the one for the hydrolysis of oximes. It is formulated as follows:

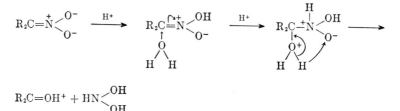

$$R_2C=OH^+ + HN\underset{OH}{\overset{OH}{\diagdown}}$$

Support for this mechanism is given by Leitch[6] who investigated the reaction with deuterated nitroethane, $CH_3CD_2NO_2$.

The adducts from acetoacetic ester and α-nitro olefins have been reported to give furans in the Nef reaction.[7]

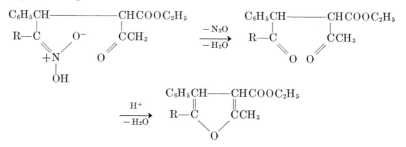

References

1. J. U. Nef, *Ann. Chem. Liebigs* **280**, 263 (1894).
2. A review of the Nef reaction is given by W. E. Noland, *Chem. Revs.* **55**, 137 (1955).
3. K. Johnson and E. F. Degering, *J. Org. Chem.* **8**, 10 (1943).
4. W. C. Wildman and R. B. Wildman, *J. Org. Chem.* **17**, 581 (1952).
5. E. E. van Tamelen and R. J. Thiede, *J. Am. Chem. Soc.* **74**, 2615 (1952).
6. L. C. Leitch, *Can. J. Chem.* **33**, 400 (1955).
7. F. Boberg and G. R. Schultze, *Chem. Ber.* **90**, 1215 (1957).

Oppenauer Oxidation

Rupert V. Oppenauer (1910–) was born in Burgstall, South Tyrol (now part of Italy). He studied at the Swiss Institute of Technology at Zurich under Ruzicka and Reichstein, and received his Ph.D. degree in 1934. He served as an assistant at Zurich, then at Amsterdam with Laqueur, and finally at Jena with Eugen Müller. After the war (1946), Oppenauer joined the faculty at Innsbruck and in 1948 became associated with Hoffmann-La Roche, Basle. At present he holds a position in the Ministry of Public Health at Buenos Aires, Argentina. Oppenauer has been particularly interested in the synthesis of sterols.

The oxidation of secondary alcohols to ketones by treatment with aluminum *tert*-butoxide (or isopropoxide) in combination with acetone is known as the Oppenauer oxidation.[1,2] This reaction, which is the reverse of the Meerwein-Ponndorf-Verley reduction, can be expressed by the general equation:

$$RR'CHOH + (CH_3)_2CO \xrightleftharpoons{\quad [(CH_3)_3CO]_3Al \quad} RR'CO + (CH_3)_2CHOH$$

Other ketones, such as cyclohexanone or methyl ethyl ketone, have been employed in place of acetone. Although some primary alcohols can be oxidized by the Oppenauer method, it is more generally applicable to secondary alcohols, particularly those in the steroid field. The oxidation is selective; other groups and carbon-carbon double bonds are not attacked.

By using a large excess of the ketone, the equilibrium can be shifted in the right direction. The aluminum derivative of the hydroxy compound to be oxidized results from an exchange reaction with the aluminum alkoxide employed. The reaction may be carried out in a solvent such as benzene or toluene at the reflux temperature. The presence of an amino group in the alcohol molecule interferes with the

177

Oppenauer oxidation.[3] This is probably due to the co-ordination of the nitrogen and aluminum.

An application of the Oppenauer oxidation which has proved valuable in the steroid series is the conversion of 3-hydroxy-Δ^5 compounds to the corresponding 3-keto-Δ^4 compounds.[4] An example of this migration of the double bond from the β,γ to the α,β position is the conversion of cholesterol to cholestenone in 70–80% yield.[5]

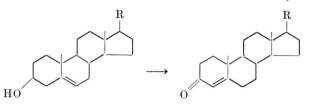

Chromic anhydride in pyridine has been found to be very effective for the oxidation of steroid alcohols.[6] This reagent (*Sarett reagent*) has been useful in converting hydroxyl to carbonyl groups without attack on double bonds and acid-sensitive groups.

References

1. R. V. Oppenauer, *Rec. trav. chim.* **56**, 137 (1937).
2. A review of the Oppenauer oxidation is given by C. Djerassi, *in* "Organic Reactions" (R. Adams, ed.), Vol. VI, p. 207. Wiley, New York, 1951.
3. R. E. Lutz and R. L. Wayland, *J. Am. Chem. Soc.* **73**, 1639 (1951).
4. W. A. Johnson and G. E. H. Skrimshire, *Chem. & Ind. (London)* p. 380 (1951).
5. R. V. Oppenauer, *in* "Organic Syntheses" (N. L. Drake, ed.), Vol. 21, p. 18. Wiley, New York, 1941.
6. G. I. Poos, G. E. Arth, R. E. Beyler, and L. H. Sarett, *J. Am. Chem. Soc.* **75**, 422 (1953).

Passerini Reaction

Mario Passerini (1891–   ) was born in Scandicci, Italy. He studied at the University of Florence, where he obtained the doctor's degree in chemistry and pharmacy. At Florence, he became an assistant in the Institute of Chemistry and Pharmacy and, later, an assistant professor. In 1930, Passerini joined the faculty at Siena. He then returned to Florence, where he has remained up to the present time.

One of Passerini's recent interests is the isolation of compounds from plant sources.

The formation of α-acyloxyanilides from an aryl isocyanide, a carbonyl compound, and a carboxylic acid is called the Passerini reaction.[1]

$$RR'CO + ArNC + R''COOH \longrightarrow RR'C-CONHAr$$
$$\underset{O-COR''}{|}$$

Alkaline hydrolysis of the product affords the α-hydroxyanilide.

It has been shown[2] that the side reactions which may occur when equimolecular quantities of the reactants are mixed at 0–25° may be avoided by performing the reaction at −20°. It has been suggested[2] that the Passerini reaction proceeds via a cyclic transition state.

$$ArNC + RR'CO \rightleftharpoons Ar\overset{+}{N}\equiv C-\underset{\underset{O^-}{|}}{C}-RR' \rightleftharpoons ArN=\overset{+}{C}-\underset{\underset{O^-}{|}}{C}-RR'$$

$$\xrightarrow{R''COOH} \quad ArN=C\text{——}C-RR' \longrightarrow ArN=C-C-RR'$$

179

When an optically-active acid was employed in the reaction,[3] an excess of one diastereomeric product was obtained, indicating an asymmetric synthesis.

References

1. M. Passerini, *Gazz. chim. ital.* **51**, 126 (1921); *Chem. Abstr.* **16**, 555 (1922).
2. R. H. Baker and D. Stanonis, *J. Am. Chem. Soc.* **73**, 699 (1951).
3. R. H. Baker and L. E. Linn, *J. Am. Chem. Soc.* **70**, 3721 (1948).

Pechmann Condensation

Hans von Pechmann (1850–1902) was born in Nürnberg, Germany. He studied at the Universities of Munich, Heidelberg, and Greifswald, where he received his doctorate (1875) under Limpricht. His thesis was on sulfonic acids of p-toluidine. Von Pechmann worked with Sir Edward Frankland at London from 1875–1877 and then with von Baeyer at Munich, where he became an assistant professor of analytical chemistry. He also taught at Tübingen (1895–1902), where he succeeded Lothar Meyer.

Von Pechmann's coumarin syntheses represent only a portion of his prolific work. He was the first to prepare many useful organic compounds including acetonedicarboxylic acid, diacetyl and other 1,2-diketones, methylglyoxal, and diazomethane. He discovered that benzoylation of diazobenzene gives nitrosobenzanilide.

Von Pechmann committed suicide by taking cyanide.

The Pechmann condensation[1,2,3] consists in the formation of coumarin derivatives from the reaction of phenols with β-keto esters in the presence of a condensing agent such as sulfuric acid, aluminum chloride, or phosphorus pentoxide.

The preparation of 4-methylcoumarin from phenol and ethyl acetoacetate is an example.[4]

Another illustration is the synthesis of methyl 5-hydroxy-4,7-dimethyl-coumarin-6-carboxylate (II) by adding concentrated sulfuric acid to a cooled mixture of methyl o-orsellinate (I) and ethyl acetoacetate.[5]

181

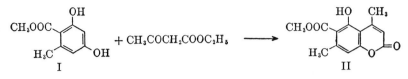

A large variety of substituted phenols and different β-keto esters have been employed in the Pechmann reaction. The ease with which phenols react depends upon the substituents in the ring. Halogens and strongly electron-attracting groups usually prevent the reaction.

Polyphosphoric acid has proved to be an excellent condensing agent for the Pechmann reaction.[6,7] The reaction of a variety of phenols with ethyl acetoacetate in the presence of this agent gives better yields of purer products than those obtained with sulfuric acid.

Cation-exchange resins such as Amberlite IR-120 have also been used as the condensing agent in the Pechmann reaction.[8] With n-hexane as the solvent the rate of the reaction is greatly increased and higher yields of coumarins are obtained.

Phenols which react with difficulty or not at all in the presence of sulfuric acid usually produce chromones with phosphorus pentoxide (*Simonis reaction*[9,10]). The yields are usually poor. Substituents on the α-position of ethyl acetoacetate favor the Simonis reaction. This is illustrated by the condensation of o-chlorophenol with ethyl α-propyl-acetoacetate to yield 8-chloro-2-methyl-3-propylchromone.[11]

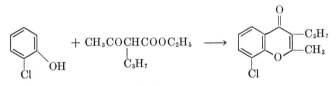

References

1. H. von Pechmann and C. Duisberg, *Ber. deut. Chem. Ges.* **16**, 2119 (1883).
2. S. M. Sethna and N. M. Shah, *Chem. Revs.* **36**, 10 (1945).
3. A review of the Pechmann reaction is given by S. Sethna and R. Phadke *in* "Organic Reactions" (R. Adams, ed.), Vol. VII, p. 1. Wiley, New York, 1953; see also S. Wawzonek *in* "Heterocyclic Compounds" (R. C. Elderfield, ed.), Vol. 2, p. 181. Wiley, New York, 1951. For a review of naturally occurring coumarins, see F. M. Dean *in* "Progress in the Chemistry of Organic Natural Products" (L. Zechmeister, ed.), Vol. IX, p. 225. Springer-Verlag, Vienna, 1952.
4. E. H. Woodruff, *in* "Organic Syntheses" (N. L. Drake, ed.), Vol. 24, p. 69. Wiley, New York, 1944.

5. P. R. Saraiya and R. C. Shah, *Proc. Indian Acad. Sci.* **31**, 213 (1950); *Chem. Abstr.* **46**, 5013 (1952).

6. J. Koo, *Chem. & Ind. (London)* p. 445 (1955).

7. R. S. Kapil and S. S. Joshi, *J. Indian Chem. Soc.* **36**, 596 (1959).

8. S. S. Israelstam and E. V. O. John, *Chem. & Ind. (London)* p. 1262 (1958).

9. E. Petschek and H. Simonis, *Ber. deut. Chem. Ges.* **46**, 2014 (1913).

10. S. M. Sethna and N. M. Shah, *Chem. Revs.* **36**, 14 (1945).

11. D. Chakravarti, *J. Indian Chem. Soc.* **9**, 25 (1932).

Perkin Reaction

Sir William Henry Perkin (1838–1907) was born in London, England. He was a student of Hofmann at the Royal College of Chemistry in London. In 1856, in his home laboratory, Perkin oxidized aniline in an effort to synthesize quinine. Instead, he discovered the dye, mauve. He started a factory for the manufacture of this dye and later prepared others, including alizarin. In 1874, Perkin retired from his successful business to devote himself to pure research. His interests covered a wide range. In addition to the Perkin reaction and the synthesis of coumarin and cinnamic acid, Perkin studied the relationship of physical properties and chemical structure, particularly the rotation of the plane of polarized light in a magnetic field.

For his notable achievements in pure research and industry, Perkin received many awards. In this country, a Perkin Medal is awarded each year by the American Section of the Society of Chemical Industry for achievement in American industrial chemistry.

The condensation of an aryl aldehyde with an anhydride in the presence of a base to give a β-substituted acrylic acid is known as the Perkin reaction.[1-3] The base is usually the sodium or potassium salt of the acid corresponding to the anhydride. An example of the reaction is the formation of cinnamic acid from benzaldehyde, acetic anhydride, and potassium acetate.

$$C_6H_5CHO + (CH_3CO)_2O \xrightarrow{CH_3COOK} C_6H_5CH{=}CHCOOH + CH_3COOH$$

The mixture is heated under reflux (175–180°) for five hours and the melt poured into water. After unreacted benzaldehyde is removed by steam distillation, the product is obtained upon acidification. Because of the conditions of the reaction, the yields are usually not very high. However, with electron-attracting substituents on the ring the yields are improved.[4]

184

Perkin assumed that the aldehyde condenses with the anhydride, the sodium acetate serving as a basic catalyst.[5] The anhydride is converted to its enolate which condenses with the aldehyde to form an aldol. Loss of water yields the unsaturated acid.

Basic catalysts other than the alkali acetates have been employed in the Perkin condensation. The use of triethylamine is illustrated in the reaction of p-hydroxybenzaldehyde with phenoxyacetic acid.[6]

$$HO\langle\rangle CHO + \langle\rangle OCH_2COOH \xrightarrow[N(C_2H_5)_3]{(CH_3CO)_2O} HO\langle\rangle CH=\overset{\overset{\displaystyle COOH}{|}}{C}-O-\langle\rangle$$

Another example is the synthesis of coumarin in 34% yield from salicylaldehyde.[7] Some o-acetoxycinnamic acid is obtained as a by-product.

$$\langle\rangle\overset{CHO}{\underset{OH}{}} + (CH_3CO)_2O \xrightarrow{N(C_2H_5)_3} \langle\rangle\underset{O}{}=O$$

The stereochemistry involved in the reaction of benzaldehyde with phenylacetic acid under Perkin conditions is discussed by Zimmerman and Ahramjian.[8] The main product in this condensation is α-phenylcinnamic acid with cis-phenyl groups. The mechanism of the reaction is depicted by the sequence:

$$C_6H_5CHO + C_6H_5CH_2COOH \xrightarrow[Et_3N]{Ac_2O} C_6H_5CHCH(C_6H_5)COOAc \longrightarrow$$
$$\underset{O-Ac}{|}$$

$$C_6H_5CH\overset{..}{C}(C_6H_5)COOAc \longrightarrow \underset{H}{\overset{C_6H_5}{}}\diagdown C=C\diagup\underset{COOAc}{\overset{C_6H_5}{}}$$
$$\underset{O-Ac}{|}$$

The reaction of unhindered aliphatic aldehydes in the Perkin reaction under mild conditions has been studied by Crawford and Little.[9]

References

1. W. H. Perkin, *J. Chem. Soc.* **21**, 53, 181 (1869); *J. Chem. Soc.* **31**, 388 (1877).
2. J. R. Johnson, *in* "Organic Reactions" (R. Adams, ed.), Vol. I, p. 210. Wiley, New York, 1942.
3. For a discussion of the Perkin reaction in connection with the Pschorr Synthesis see, P. H. Leake, *Chem. Revs.* **56**, 27 (1956).

4. G. Lock and E. Bayer, *Ber. deut. Chem. Ges.* **72,** 1064 (1939).
5. For a discussion of the mechanism of the Perkin reaction, see D. S. Breslow and C. R. Hauser, *J. Am. Chem. Soc.* **61,** 786, 793 (1939); and, V. Franzen, *Chem. Ztg.* **80,** 166 (1956).
6. D. Papa and E. Schwenk, U. S. Patent 2,503,296 (Apr. 11, 1950); *Chem. Abstr.* **44,** 6886 (1950).
7. R. E. Buckles, *J. Chem. Educ.* **27,** 210 (1950).
8. H. E. Zimmerman and L. Ahramjian, *J. Am. Chem. Soc.* **81,** 2086 (1959).
9. M. Crawford and W. T. Little, *J. Chem. Soc.* p. 722 (1959).

Pfitzinger Reaction

Wilhelm Pfitzinger began his work on the preparation of cinchoninic acids from isatinic acid and ketones in 1885 at Leipzig. In 1888 he was apparently employed at the dyestuff company, Friedrich Bayer & Co., Elberfeld. Pfitzinger continued his research on his quinoline synthesis (1892–1897) in the laboratory of E. von Meyer, who was professor of chemistry at the Technische Hochschule at Dresden. In 1902, he reported on the reaction of isatinic acid with aldehyde oximes, from the Institute of Technology at Berlin.

The formation of cinchoninic acid derivatives (III) from isatin (I) or isatinic acid (II) and a compound containing the structure —CH$_2$CO— is known as the Pfitzinger reaction.[1,2] The general reaction is illustrated by the following equations:

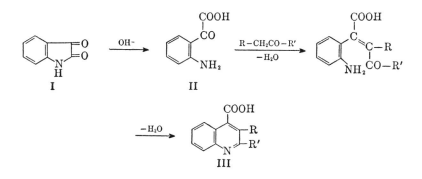

The reaction is similar to the Friedländer synthesis in which the starting material is an *o*-aminobenzaldehyde or *o*-aminophenyl ketone.

In the Pfitzinger reaction with methyl ketones other than methyl ethyl ketone, the methyl group is usually involved in the condensa-

187

tion.[3] For example, the reaction of isatin with methyl *n*-propyl ketone gives as the main product 2-*n*-propylcinchoninic acid.

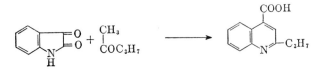

Isomeric 2,3-disubstituted cinchoninic acids have been isolated and identified from the reaction with unsymmetrical *n*-alkyl methyl ketones.[4] Some 2-substituted long-chain alkyl derivatives have recently been prepared.[5]

It has been shown that in many instances pyrolysis of the cinchoninic acid gives the expected 2-alkylquinoline and also the corresponding 4-hydroxyquinoline.[3]

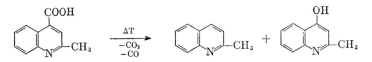

The reaction of certain propoxymethyl ketones with isatin yields the 2-alkyl-3-propoxycinchoninic acid (IV), where R is ethyl or higher homologs.[6]

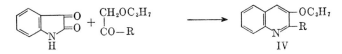

Mueller and Stobaugh[7] reported on the effect of steric hindrance in the Pfitzinger reaction.[8] The trimethyldesoxybenzoin (V) could not be condensed with isatin.

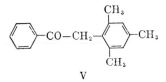

V

References

1. W. Pfitzinger, *J. prakt. Chem.* 33, 100 (1886); 38, 582 (1888).
2. See R. H. Manske, *Chem. Revs.* 30, 126 (1942); R. C. Elderfield, ed., *in* "Heterocyclic Compounds," Vol. 4, p. 47. Wiley, New York, 1952.

3. Ng. Ph. Buu-Hoï and R. Royer, *J. Chem. Soc.* p. 106 (1948).
4. H. R. Henze and D. W. Carroll, *J. Am. Chem. Soc.* **76,** 4580 (1954).
5. Ng. Ph. Buu-Hoï and P. Jacquignon, *Bull. soc. chim. France* p. 1567 (1958).
6. H. R. Henze, J. W. Melton, and E. O. Forman, *J. Am. Chem. Soc.* **70,** 2622 (1948).
7. G. P. Mueller and R. E. Stobaugh, *J. Am. Chem. Soc.* **72,** 1598 (1950).
8. See also Ng. Ph. Buu-Hoï, R. Royer, Ng. D. Xuong, and P. Jacquignon, *J. Org. Chem.* **18,** 1209 (1953).

Pictet-Spengler Reaction

Amé Pictet (1857–1937) was born in Geneva, Switzerland. He studied at Geneva, Dresden, Bonn, and Paris, and received the doctor's degree under Graebe at Geneva in 1881. There he joined the faculty and in 1899 became professor of biological and pharmaceutical chemistry.

Pictet's interest in the chemistry of plant alkaloids led to his synthesis of nicotine, laudanosine, and papaverine. His later years were devoted to carbohydrate chemistry.

The condensation of β-arylethylamines with carbonyl compounds to give tetrahydroisoquinolines is called the Pictet-Spengler reaction.[1,2] Of the aldehydes employed in the synthesis, formaldehyde has given the most satisfactory results. The Schiff base which is initially formed may be isolated in some instances or cyclized directly by heating with aqueous hydrochloric acid.

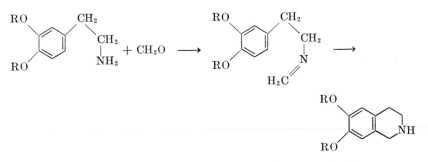

The activation in the *ortho* position by a methoxy or a hydroxy group is similar to that described for the Bischler-Napieralski reaction (p. 20).

In many cases the Pictet-Spengler reaction has been carried out under conditions of acidity, temperature, and concentration which

190

approach plant environment. This type of synthesis may be involved in the formation of isoquinoline alkaloids in plants.

References

1. A. Pictet and T. Spengler, *Ber. deut. Chem. Ges.* **44**, 2030 (1911).
2. A review of the reaction is given by W. M. Whaley and T. R. Govindachari, *in* "Organic Reactions" (R. Adams, ed.), Vol. VI, p. 151. Wiley, New York, 1951; see also, W. J. Gensler, *in* "Heterocyclic Compounds" (R. C. Elderfield, ed.), Vol. 4, pp. 353–361. Wiley, New York, 1952.

Pomeranz-Fritsch Reaction

Cesar Pomeranz (1860–1926) received the Ph.D. degree at Vienna, where he became an associate professor of chemistry. Later, he served as professor of chemistry at the University of Czernovitz, Bukovina.

* * *

Paul Fritsch (1859–1913) was born in Oels, Silesia. He studied at Berlin and Munich, where he received the doctorate degree in 1884. He served as an assistant at Munich, Breslau, Rostock, and then at Marburg, where he became professor of chemistry. Fritsch's work included investigations of condensations with chloral and the synthesis of substituted aromatic acids, aromatic amines, and triphenylmethane derivatives.

The cyclization of benzalaminoacetals with sulfuric acid to yield isoquinolines is called the Pomeranz-Fritsch reaction.[1] Sulfuric acid alone or in combination with such acidic reagents as hydrogen chloride, phosphorus oxychloride, or acetic acid have been employed in the reaction.[2]

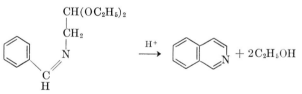

The benzalaminoacetal is prepared from the appropriate aromatic aldehyde with aminoacetal. A modification introduced by Schlittler and Müller[3] involves the reaction of a benzylamine with glyoxal semiacetal.

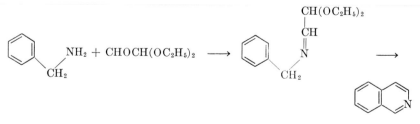

192

The best yields in the Pomeranz-Fritsch reaction are obtained with *m*-hydroxy-, *m*-alkoxy-, or *m*-halobenzalaminoacetals. Substituents on the *ortho* or *para* positions give poor yields of the desired isoquinoline derivative or no product at all.

Papaveraldine, which can be reduced to papaverine, has recently been prepared in 8% yield from the crude mono-Schiff base, N-(α-veratroylveratrylidene)aminoacetal.[4] The cyclization was carried out with 72% sulfuric acid at room temperature. The temperature and acid concentration appear to be critical.

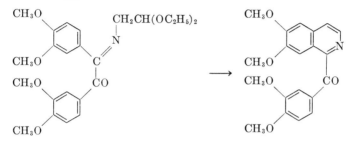

Vinot[5] has described the preparation of isoquinoline derivatives from the reaction of benzylaminoacetals in the presence of boron trifluoride.

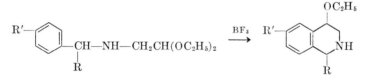

References

1. C. Pomeranz, *Monatsh. Chem.* **14**, 116 (1893); P. Fritsch, *Ber. deut. Chem. Ges.* **26**, 419 (1893).
2. A review of the Pomeranz-Fritsch reaction is given by W. J. Gensler, *in* "Organic Reactions" (R. Adams, ed.), Vol. VI, p. 191. Wiley, New York, 1951; see, also, W. J. Gensler, *in* "Heterocyclic Compounds" (R. C. Elderfield, ed.), Vol. 4, pp. 368–372. Wiley, New York, 1952.
3. E. Schlittler and J. Müller, *Helv. Chim. Acta* **31**, 914 (1948).
4. D. A. Guthrie, A. W. Frank, and C. B. Purves, *Can. J. Chem.* **33**, 729 (1955).
5. N. Vinot, *Ann. chim.* (*Paris*) [13] **3**, 461 (1958).

Prins Reaction

Hendrik Jacobus Prins (1889–1958) was born in Zaandam, The Netherlands. He studied at the Delft Technical Institute where he received the chemical engineering degree in 1911 and the doctor's degree a year later under J. Boeseken. Prins took a position as chemist in an essential oil company, and then in 1924 joined the Nederlandsche Thermo-Chemische Fabrieken, a company that deals with the rendering of condemned meats and carcasses. He rose to the position of president-director of this firm. For his contributions as manager Prins was appointed "Officier in de Orde von Orange Nassau" by the Dutch government.

Prins had a small laboratory near his house where he carried out his experiments in his spare time. His main interest in organic chemistry centered around polychloro compounds.

The acid-catalyzed condensation of an aldehyde with an olefin is usually referred to as Prins reaction.[1] With formaldehyde, the reaction appears to be general, but the course of the reaction is greatly influenced by the type of catalyst and the conditions employed.[2] The following are the three classifications of the reaction which are most often encountered:

The acid-catalyzed condensation. When a mineral acid, usually sulfuric acid, is used as a catalyst and water is the solvent, *m*-dioxanes and 1,3-glycols are the main products.

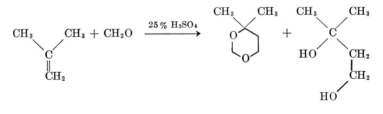

194

By a suitable choice of reaction conditions, one product can be made to predominate, as in the preparation of 4-phenyl-*m*-dioxane in 71–88% yield from styrene.[3] 1,3-Glycols may be obtained as the major product from the reaction of aldehydes with primary olefins by control of temperature (above 70°), catalyst strength, and reaction time.[4] When acetic acid is used as a solvent in the reaction, the diacetate of the corresponding 1,3-glycol is one of the products obtained.

The Prins reaction with *trans*-cinnamic acid in acetic-sulfuric acid solution at 80° is reported to give 4-phenyl-1,3-dioxane-5-carboxylic acid in 25% yield.[5] After a Hofmann reaction on the corresponding amide the ring was opened with phloroglucinol and hydrochloric acid to yield a 1,3-glycol derivative. The Prins reaction with ω-nitrostyrene was unsuccessful.

The metallic halide-catalyzed condensation. Under anhydrous condensation conditions, some tertiary olefins containing four to eight carbon atoms react with formaldehyde to yield unsaturated alcohols.[6]

$$(CH_3)_2C{=}CH_2 + CH_2O \xrightarrow{SnCl_4} \overset{\displaystyle CH_3}{\underset{\displaystyle |}{CH_2{=}C}}{-}CH_2{-}CH_2OH$$

This reaction is catalyzed by such halides as stannic chloride, zinc chloride, and silicon tetrachloride. On the other hand, *m*-dioxanes may result when aluminum chloride or ferric chloride is used as a catalyst. Primary olefins or the higher aldehydes react to form alkyl *m*-dioxanes.

The thermal condensation. When tertiary olefins are heated with formaldehyde in the absence of a catalyst, unsaturated alcohols are produced.[7] Methylenecyclohexane reacts with formaldehyde in a sealed tube at 200° to give 2-(1-cyclohexenyl) ethanol.

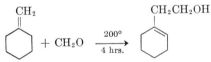

The optimum temperatures of this reaction appear to be in the range of 180–200°. In the presence of glacial acetic acid, the acetate of the unsaturated alcohol is formed.

The congruity of the above reactions is demonstrated by the mechanism for the Prins reaction recently proposed by Yang.[8] This mechanism assumes that a polarized addition complex of formaldehyde adds to the olefin according to the Markownikoff rule. The intermediate may then react (a) through a 6-membered cyclic mechanism to give rise to the unsaturated alcohol, or (b) with the solvent or formaldehyde to form the glycol, ester, or *m*-dioxane.

$$HCHO + A \rightleftharpoons \overset{\oplus}{H_2C}-O-\overset{\ominus}{A} \qquad A = SnCl_4 \text{ or other acids}$$

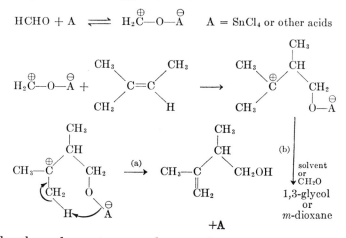

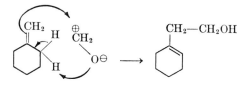

The thermal reaction may be considered to take place through the polarized formaldehyde molecule, which is essentially the concerted mechanism proposed by Arnold and Dowdall.[7]

The stereochemical course of the Prins reaction has been investigated by several authors.[9-11] The acid-catalyzed condensation of cyclohexene with formaldehyde was shown to involve a *trans*-diaxial addition to the double bond. The major products isolated from this reaction[11] are *trans*-2-hydroxymethyl-1-cyclohexanol, and *trans*-4,5-tetramethylene-1,3-dioxane.

Ketones are formed by a fourth aldehyde-olefin condensation catalyzed by peroxides. Best yields are obtained from both higher molecular-weight aldehydes and higher molecular-weight terminal olefins.[12]

References

1. H. J. Prins, *Chem. Weekblad* **14**, 627 (1917).
2. A comprehensive review of the Prins reaction is given by E. Arundale and L. A. Mikeska, *Chem. Revs.* **51**, 505 (1952).

196

3. R. L. Shriner and P. R. Ruby, *in* "Organic Syntheses" (C. C. Prise, ed.), Vol. 33, p. 72. Wiley, New York, 1953.
4. L. A. Mikeska and E. Arundale, U. S. Patent, 2,449,001 (Sept. 7, 1948); *Chem. Abstr.* **43**, 673 (1949).
5. F. W. Brugman and J. F. Areus, *Rec. trav. chim.* **74**, 209 (1955).
6. E. Arundale and L. A. Mikeska, *Chem. Revs.* **51**, 532–534 (1952).
7. R. T. Arnold and J. F. Dowdall, *J. Am. Chem. Soc.* **70**, 2590 (1948).
8. N. C. Yang, D. H. Yang, and C. B. Ross, *J. Am. Chem. Soc.* **81**, 133 (1959).
9. G. Fodor, O. Kovacs, I. Tomoskozi, and J. Szilagyi, *Bull. soc. chim. France* p. 357 (1957).
10. E. E. Smissman and R. A. Mode, *J. Am. Chem. Soc.* **79**, 3447 (1957).
11. A. T. Blomquist and J. Woliusky, *J. Am. Chem. Soc.* **79**, 6025 (1957)
12. E. Arundale and L. A. Mikeska, *Chem. Revs.* **51**, 544–546 (1952).

197

Pschorr Synthesis

Robert Pschorr (1868–1930) was born in Munich, Germany. He studied chemistry at Munich under von Baeyer and at Zurich under Bamberger. In 1892, he went to Jena to complete his studies under Knorr. There he worked on the synthesis of pyrazoles and prepared 4-ketopyrazolone. He then turned his attention to a study of the opium alkaloids. After a trip around the world, Pschorr worked under Fischer at Berlin, where he became an assistant professor in 1899. It was during a study of phenanthrene chemistry in relation to the morphine problem that Pschorr discovered his well-known phenanthrene synthesis. He also investigated the degradation of apomorphine and thebaine.

Pschorr succeeded Liebermann in the chair of organic chemistry at the Technical Institute Berlin-Charlottenburg (1913), where in 1920 he was appointed president. During World War I Pschorr served as a major.

The Pschorr synthesis[1-4] consists in the preparation of phenanthrene derivatives starting with an *o*-nitrobenzaldehyde and an arylacetic acid. The first step leads to an α-phenyl-*o*-nitrocinnamic acid.

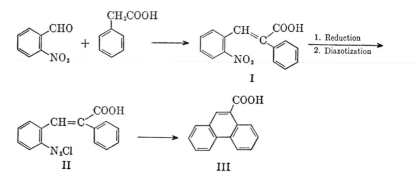

Reduction to the amine followed by diazotization gives the diazonium compound II, which on treatment with copper powder loses nitrogen and hydrogen chloride to yield a phenanthrene-9-carboxylic acid.

The synthesis has a wide scope. A variety of phenanthrenes have been prepared by this method from substituted *o*-nitrobenzaldehydes and phenylacetic acids. With naphthylacetic acid, benzphenanthrenes are obtained. Analogous cyclizations are useful for preparing carbazoles, fluorenes, and fluorenones.[5] An example of the latter is the synthesis of 3-bromofluorenone.[6] The Pschorr synthesis has been

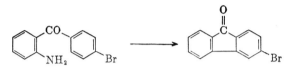

especially useful in structure determination of naturally-occurring materials, especially the opium alkaloids.[7]

Hey and Osbond[8] have shown that the synthesis can be carried out satisfactorily under a variety of modifications of the original procedure. In addition, the reaction has been successfully employed in the synthesis of a heterocyclic nucleus in which the final ring closure involves a pyridine ring. These authors have also demonstrated that deactivating groups such as NO_2, CN, or COOH in the α-phenyl nucleus do not interfere with the reaction. This is offered as support for a free-radical mechanism for the Pschorr synthesis.

References

1. R. Pschorr, *Ber. deut. Chem. Ges.* **29**, 496 (1896).
2. K. H. Saunders, "Reactions of the Diazo-Compounds," pp. 254–258. Arnold, London, 1949.
3. P. H. Leake, *Chem. Revs.* **56**, 27 (1956).
4. A review of the Pschorr synthesis and related diazonium ring closure reactions is given by D. F. deTar, *in* "Organic Reactions" (R. Adams, ed.), Vol. IX, p. 37. Wiley, New York, 1957.
5. H. H. Hodgson, *J. Chem. Soc.* p. 348 (1948); K. H. Saunders, "Reactions of the Diazo-Compounds," pp. 258–267. Arnold, London, 1949.
6. H. F. Miller and G. B. Bachmann, *J. Am. Chem. Soc.* **57**, 2443 (1935).
7. See L. F. Fieser and M. Fieser, "Natural Products Related to Phenanthrene," American Chemical Society Monograph No. 70, p. 8. Reinhold, New York, 1949.
8. D. H. Hey and J. M. Osbond, *J. Chem. Soc.* pp. 3164, 3172 (1949).

Reformatsky Reaction

Sergius Reformatsky (1860–1934) was born in Russia. He studied under Saitzeff at the University of Kasan, where he became an assistant professor (1886). Later he studied at Göttingen, at Heidelberg under Victor Meyer, and at Leipzig under Ostwald. He received his doctor's degree in 1891 and returned to Russia to assume the chair of organic chemistry at Kiev. From 1931, Reformatsky worked at the Kiev Institute for Rubber Research.

His most important work was in the field of β-hydroxy acids where zinc organic compounds were used. Reformatsky was also interested in substituted glutaric acids, polyhydric alcohols, and problems concerning stereoisomerism.

A method of preparing β-hydroxy esters and the corresponding unsaturated esters by the reaction of α-halo esters with aldehydes or ketones in the presence of zinc is known as the Reformatsky reaction.[1,2] The condensation, which has had wide application, is usually carried out by the addition of a mixture of the reactants in an inert solvent, such as ether, benzene, or toluene, to the zinc at a rate just sufficient to maintain gentle refluxing. External heating is generally employed to start the reaction. The organo-complex formed in the reaction is hydrolyzed with dilute acid. An example of the Reformatsky reaction is the synthesis of ethyl α-methyl-β-phenyl-β-hydroxybutyrate from ethyl α-bromopropionate, acetophenone, and zinc.

$$\underset{\displaystyle |}{\overset{\displaystyle CH_3}{\underset{\displaystyle BrCH}{|}}}—COOC_2H_5 + Zn \longrightarrow \overset{\displaystyle CH_3}{\underset{\displaystyle BrZnCH}{|}}—COOC_2H_5$$

$$\overset{\displaystyle CH_3}{\underset{\displaystyle BrZnCH}{|}}—COOC_2H_5 + C_6H_5COCH_3 \longrightarrow \underset{\displaystyle OZnBr}{\overset{\displaystyle H_3C \quad CH_3}{C_6H_5C—CH}}—COOC_2H_5 \longrightarrow$$

$$\underset{\displaystyle OH}{\overset{\displaystyle H_3C \quad CH_3}{C_6H_5C—CH}}—COOC_2H_5$$

The hydroxy esters can be converted to the corresponding unsaturated esters by heating with a dehydrating agent such as acetic anhydride, dry hydrogen chloride, or many other dehydrating agents.

The dehydration usually results in the formation of an α,β-unsaturated ester or acid. However, in many instances, both α,β- and β,γ-unsaturated products are obtained. The composition of the mixture depends on the structure of the β-hydroxy ester and the dehydrating agent employed.

For the most part, the Reformatsky reaction has been restricted to the use of the α-bromo ester, and occasionally magnesium has been employed in place of zinc. From a study of the scope of the Reformatsky reaction, Miller and Nord[3] demonstrated that the reaction can be extended to include the use of α-chloroacetates and β-bromo esters, provided that a suitable promoting agent is present. In a series of metallic halides investigated, mercuric chloride was found to be the most effective promotor. β-Bromoethyl acetate has also been employed in the Reformatsky reaction.[3] The products obtained from the reaction of this halo ester with aldehydes and ketones are α,β-unsaturated alcohols.

$$\underset{R'}{\overset{R}{\diagdown}}C{=}O + BrCH_2CH_2O\overset{\overset{O}{\|}}{C}{-}CH_3 \xrightarrow{Mg} \left[\underset{R'}{\overset{R}{\diagdown}}C{=}CHCH_2O\overset{\overset{O}{\|}}{C}{-}CH_3\right] \xrightarrow{OH^-}$$

$$\underset{R'}{\overset{R}{\diagdown}}C{=}CHCH_2OH$$

Hussey and Newman[4] have investigated some side reactions and their products which may occur in the Reformatsky reaction. An explanation for improved yields using an excess of zinc and bromo ester is also given.

The formation of two diastereoisomers has been demonstrated in the synthesis of α-ethyl-β-phenylacrylic acid from ethyl α-bromobutyrate and benzaldehyde.[5]

$$C_6H_5CHO + \underset{\overset{|}{Br}}{\overset{\overset{CH_2CH_3}{|}}{CH}}{-}COOR \longrightarrow C_6H_5CH{=}\overset{\overset{CH_2CH_3}{|}}{C}{-}COOH$$

201

References

1. S. Reformatsky, *Ber. deut. Chem. Ges.* **20**, 1210 (1887); *J. prakt. Chem.* **54**, 469 (1896).
2. A review of the Reformatsky reaction is given by R. L. Shriner, *in* "Organic Reactions" (R. Adams, ed.), Vol. I, p. 1. Wiley, New York, 1942.
3. R. E. Miller and F. F. Nord, *J. Org. Chem.* **16**, 728 (1951).
4. A. S. Hussey and M. S. Newman, *J. Am. Chem. Soc.* **70**, 3024 (1948).
5. L. Canonica and F. Pelizzoni, *Gazz. chim. ital.* **84**, 553 (1954); *Chem. Abstr.* **50**, 879 (1956).

Reimer-Tiemann Reaction

Karl Ludwig Reimer (1845–1883) was born in Leipzig, Germany. He studied at Göttingen and Greifswald. After serving in the Bohemian War (1866) he returned to Greifswald. From there he went to Heidelberg and then to Berlin, where he obtained the Ph.D. degree in 1871. Reimer became an instructor in a forestry academy and later was employed as a chemist in the Kahlbaum Co. In 1876, he joined the Vanillin Co. as a partner. Five years later he resigned because of poor health.

Reimer's discovery of the formation of salicylaldehyde from phenol and chloroform (1875) made this material available for the first time in large quantities. This work was the beginning of Reimer's short-lived career in organic chemistry.

* * *

Johann Karl Ferdinand Tiemann (1848–1899) was born in Rübeland, Germany. He was a student of Hofmann at Berlin, where he received the doctorate degree and later became professor of chemistry. Tiemann was greatly influenced by Hofmann, with whom he was associated for many years.

He is known for his researches on nitriles and terpenes. His synthesis of vanillin, applying Reimer's reaction for the preparation of o-hydroxyaldehydes, had a profound influence on the perfume industry. His isolation of irone, the aromatic principle of violet root, led to the preparation of the perfume ionone.

The Reimer-Tiemann reaction[1] consists in the introduction of a formyl group by heating a phenolic compound with chloroform in the presence of alkali. An illustration is the preparation of salicylaldehyde from phenol and chloroform.[2]

$$\text{C}_6\text{H}_5\text{OH} + \text{CHCl}_3 + 3\text{KOH} \longrightarrow \text{C}_6\text{H}_4(\text{OH})(\text{CHO}) + 3\text{KCl} + 2\text{H}_2\text{O}$$

Although the usual product in the Reimer-Tiemann reaction is the *o*-formyl derivative of the phenol, some of the *para* isomer is also obtained. This is especially true where an *ortho* position is occupied. In the above illustration, if carbon tetrachloride is employed instead of chloroform and the reaction mixture is heated at 100° in a sealed tube, the products are salicylic acid and *p*-hydroxybenzoic acid. Another example of the Reimer-Tiemann reaction is the conversion of β-naphthol to 2-hydroxy-1-naphthaldehyde in 38–48% yield.[3]

The scope of the Reimer-Tiemann reaction is rather limited. Electron-attracting substituents on the aromatic ring interfere with the reaction. The yield of the desired product is usually low. In certain instances other products are obtained which give some insight into the possible mechanism of the reaction. For example, in the reaction of *p*-cresol with chloroform, two products were isolated.[4]

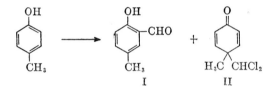

The formation of the ketone (II) would indicate that a dichloromethyl intermediate may be involved in the Reimer-Tiemann reaction.

Woodward[5] has shown that (*ar*)-β-tetralol can be converted to *trans*-10-methyl-2-decalone by a so-called abnormal Reimer-Tiemann reaction.

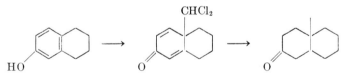

This procedure has been extended to the preparation of *trans*-9-methyl-1-decalone via the dienone intermediate.[6]

The formation of two isomeric dienones from mesitol along with a small amount of mesityl orthoformate is also reported.

A review of the Reimer-Tiemann reaction has been reported recently by Wynberg.[7]

References

1. K. Reimer, *Ber. deut. Chem. Ges.* **9,** 423 (1876); K. Reimer and F. Tiemann, *Ber. deut. Chem. Ges.* **9,** 824 (1876).
2. K. Reimer and F. Tiemann, *Ber. deut. Chem. Ges.* **9,** 1285 (1876).
3. A. Russell and L. B. Lockhart, *in* "Organic Syntheses" (L. I. Smith, ed.), Vol. 22, p. 63. Wiley, New York, 1942.
4. K. Auwers and F. Winternitz, *Ber. deut. Chem. Ges.* **35,** 465 (1902).
5. R. B. Woodward, *J. Am. Chem. Soc.* **62,** 1208 (1940).
6. H. Wynberg and W. S. Johnson, *J. Org. Chem.* **24,** 1424 (1959).
7. H. Wynberg, *Chem. Revs.* **60,** 169 (1960).

Reissert Reaction

Carl Arnold Reissert (1860– ?) was born in Powayen, Germany. He studied at Heidelberg, at Königsberg, and at Berlin, where he received his doctor's degree in 1884. Four years later he was appointed assistant professor of chemistry. At Berlin, Reissert collaborated with Tiemann. In 1902, he joined the faculty at Marburg, where he became associate professor in 1922.

The Reissert reaction[1] consists in treating an acid chloride with potassium cyanide (or hydrogen cyanide) in the presence of quinoline and hydrolyzing the resulting 1-acyl-2-cyano-1,2-dihydroquinoline with acid to give an aldehyde and quinaldic acid.

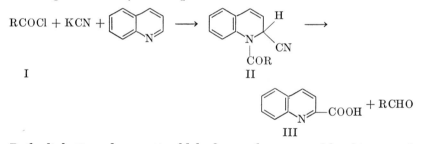

Both aliphatic and aromatic aldehydes can be prepared by this general method.[2] The reaction has also been employed for the preparation of some quinaldonitriles starting with N-oxides of quinoline.[3]

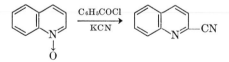

McEwen and Hazlett[4] have investigated the acid-catalyzed formation of aldehydes from Reissert compounds (II) and have proposed the following mechanism.

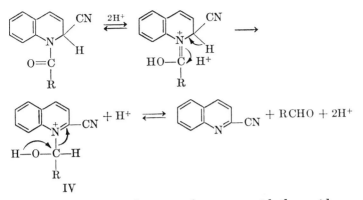

IV

The first step involves coordination of a proton with the amide oxygen. The loss of a proton from the 2 position in the quinoline ring and the addition of a proton to the carbonyl carbon atom leads to the intermediate (IV) which dissociates to give the aldehyde and nitrile. The presence of the 3,4- double bond in the Reissert compound appears to be essential for the formation of the aromatic aldehyde.[5]

Davis[6] has recently prepared quinaldic acid in quantitative yield from the Reissert compound, 1-benzoyl-1,2-dihydroquinaldonitrile, (II, R = C_6H_5) by hydrolysis with hydrobromic acid in acetic acid as the reaction medium. Benzaldehyde was also obtained in high yield.

References

1. A. Reissert, *Ber. deut. Chem. Ges.* **38**, 1603, 3415 (1905).
2. A review of the Reissert reaction is given by W. E. McEwen and R. Cobb, *Chem. Revs.* **55**, 511 (1955). The Reissert reaction is included in a review of syntheses of aldehydes from carboxylic acids, by E. Mossetig, *in* "Organic Reactions" (R. Adams, ed.), Vol. VIII, p. 218. Wiley, New York, 1954.
3. M. Henze, *Ber. deut. Chem. Ges.* **69**, 1566 (1936); E. Ochiai and I. Nakayama, *Chem. Abstr.* **45**, 8529 (1951).
4. W. E. McEwen and R. N. Hazlett, *J. Am. Chem. Soc.* **71**, 1949 (1949).
5. R. F. Collins and T. Henshall, *J. Chem. Soc.* p. 1881 (1956).
6. J. W. Davis, *J. Org. Chem.* **24**, 1691 (1959).

Rosenmund Reduction

Karl Wilhelm Rosenmund (1884–   ) was born in Berlin, Germany. At the University there he was a student of O. Diels. He received the doctor's degree in 1906 and later became professor of chemistry. In 1925 he was appointed professor and director of the Pharamaceutical Institute at Kiel.

Rosenmund is well-known for his work on amino phenolic ketones, his method of reduction of acid chlorides, and his synthesis of phenylarsonic acids from the reaction of halobenzenes with tripotassium arsenite (*Rosenmund reaction*).

The reduction of an acid chloride to an aldehyde in the presence of a palladium catalyst is referred to as the Rosenmund reduction.[1,2] An illustration is the preparation of β-naphthaldehyde from β-naphthoyl chloride.[3]

The reduction is usually carried out by bubbling hydrogen into a stirred and refluxing solution of the acid chloride in an inert solvent such as toluene or xylene. In most instances, the catalyst employed is 5% palladium-on-barium sulfate. The hydrogen chloride which is evolved during the reduction can be collected in alkali and titrated. In this way the reaction can be followed and heating stopped when no further evidence of hydrogen chloride evolution is observed.

The Rosenmund reduction offers a very satisfactory method of converting both aliphatic and aromatic acid chlorides to the corresponding aldehydes. In the presence of a sulfur-quinoline poison, other substituents, such as nitro or chloro, are not affected.[4] Half-aldehydes of dibasic acids have been prepared[5] using palladium-on-charcoal as the catalyst.

208

References

1. K. W. Rosenmund, *Ber. deut. Chem. Ges.* **51**, 585 (1918).
2. A review of the Rosenmund reduction is given by E. Mosettig and R. Mozingo, *in* "Organic Reactions" (R. Adams, ed.), Vol. IV, p. 362. Wiley, New York, 1948.
3. E. B. Hershberg and J. Cason, *in* "Organic Syntheses" (N. L. Drake, ed.), Vol. 21, p. 84. Wiley, New York, 1941.
4. Lithium tri-*tert*-butoxyaluminum hydride has been found to be an effective reagent for the reduction of acid chlorides to aldehydes. H. C. Brown and R. F. McFarlin, *J. Am. Chem. Soc.* **80**, 5372 (1958).
5. F. C. Pennington, W. D. Celmer, M. M. McLamore, V. V. Bogert, and I. A. Solomons, *J. Am. Chem. Soc.* **75**, 109 (1953).

Sandmeyer Reaction

Traugott Sandmeyer (1854–1922) was born in Wettingen, Switzerland. He received some of his early scientific training in an engineering workshop. In 1882, he became a lecture-assistant to Victor Meyer at Zurich, where he carried out some of his research. Three years later Sandmeyer accompanied Meyer to Göttingen and then returned to Zurich as assistant to Hantzsch. In 1888, he joined the firm of J. R. Geigy, where he remained for 31 years. At the age of 37, Sandmeyer received an honorary Ph.D. degree from the University of Heidelberg.

Sandmeyer is best known for his Sandmeyer reaction and for his many discoveries in the dye industry, especially in the field of triphenylmethane dyes. Some of the methods he developed in this field are used today. Sandmeyer also discovered a new method for manufacturing isatins in quantitative yields starting with amines, chloral, and hydroxylamines.[1]

Although it is generally accepted that Victor Meyer discovered thiophene, it was Sandmeyer, his assistant, who suggested that there must be something present in technical benzene that is responsible for the isatin reaction with concentrated sulfuric acid.

In 1884[2] Sandmeyer discovered that aromatic diazonium salts are readily decomposed by heating with cuprous chloride in the presence of hydrochloric acid to yield an aromatic chloro compound.

$$C_6H_5NH_2 \xrightarrow[\text{HCl}]{\text{NaNO}_2} C_6H_5N_2Cl \xrightarrow[\text{HCl}]{\text{Cu}_2\text{Cl}_2} C_6H_5Cl + N_2$$

The Sandmeyer reaction[3] is usually carried out by adding the cold diazonium salt solution to a solution of one equivalent of cuprous chloride in hydrochloric acid and warming. With cuprous bromide or cuprous cyanide the corresponding bromo or cyano derivatives can be prepared.

210

$$C_6H_5N_2SO_3H \xrightarrow[\text{HBr}]{\text{Cu}_2\text{Br}_2} C_6H_5Br$$

$$C_6H_5N_2Cl \xrightarrow[\text{KCN}]{\text{Cu}_2(\text{CN})_2} C_6H_5CN$$

The reaction has also been employed for the replacement of a diazonium salt by the following groups: SCN, NO_2, SH, N_3, AsO_3H_2,[4] and F.[5]

Hodgson and Norris[6] have reported on the preparation of chloro- and bromophenols by a modification of the Sandmeyer reaction. The nitroso group in p-nitrosophenols is replaced by halogen by the reaction with hydroxylamine salts in the presence of cuprous salts and the appropriate halogen acid.

With active nitroso compounds, nitrogen is readily evolved. Other aryl nitroso compounds require heating.

Cowdrey and Davies[7] investigated the kinetics of the Sandmeyer reaction for replacing diazonium groups by halogen. On the basis of these studies a mechanism was proposed which is not in agreement with previous proposals. According to these workers, the reaction is first-order with respect to both diazonium ion and dissolved cuprous chloride. The $CuCl_2^-$ ion is the catalyst which reacts with the ArN_2^+ ion, probably by co-ordination of the Cu with the terminal nitrogen.

$$ArN_2^+ + CuCl_2^- \longrightarrow [ArN_2\!-\!CuCl_2]$$

This complex decomposes rapidly to yield the product ArCl.

$$[ArN_2\!-\!CuCl_2] \longrightarrow ArCl + N_2 + CuCl$$

The fact that electron-attracting groups on the aryl nucleus increase the rate of the reaction and the formation of an azo compound as a by-product can be explained by this interpretation of the Sandmeyer reaction.[8]

References

1. German Patents 113,848, 113,981 (1899).
2. T. Sandmeyer, *Ber. deut. Chem. Ges.* **17**, 1633 (1884); *Ber. deut. Chem. Ges.* **23**, 1880 (1890).

3. A review of the Sandmeyer reaction is given by H. H. Hodgson, *Chem. Revs.* **40**, 251 (1947); see, also, W. A. Cowdrey and D. S. Davies, *Quart. Revs. (London)* **6**, 358 (1952).
4. See Bart reaction, p. 10.
5. See Schiemann reaction, p. 213.
6. H. H. Hodgson and W. H. H. Norris, *J. Chem. Soc.* p. S181 (1949).
7. W. A. Cowdrey and D. S. Davies, *J. Chem. Soc.* p. S48 (1949).
8. For a detailed account of the mechanism of diazotization of primary aromatic amines, see E. D. Hughes, C. K. Ingold, and J. H. Ridd, *J. Chem. Soc.* p. 58, (1958).

Schiemann Reaction

Günther Robert Arthur Schiemann (1899–   ) was born in Breslau. He studied at the University there as well as in Freiburg and the Technische Hochschule at Breslau. In 1925 he received his doctorate degree from Breslau and became an assistant in organic chemistry. Four years later, Schiemann was appointed assistant professor at the Technische Hochschule at Hanover. In 1950, he was called to assume the chair of technical chemistry at Istanbul.

Schiemann has been particularly interested in the preparation and reactions of aromatic fluorine compounds.

The pyrolytic decomposition of an aromatic diazonium fluoroborate to yield an aromatic fluoride, nitrogen, and boron trifluoride is known as the Schiemann reaction.[1] The reaction is a very satisfactory method for replacing a diazonium salt group by fluorine.[2]

$$C_6H_5NH_2 \xrightarrow[HCl]{NaNO_2} C_6H_5N_2Cl$$

$$C_6H_5N_2Cl \xrightarrow{HBF_4} C_6H_5N_2BF_4$$

$$C_6H_5N_2BF_4 \longrightarrow C_6H_5F + N_2 + BF_3$$

The aromatic amine is diazotized in the usual manner, and the diazonium salt solution is treated with fluoroboric acid (or sodium fluoroborate) to precipitate the diazonium fluoroborate. Another method is to perform the diazotization in the presence of fluoroboric acid. The insoluble diazonium fluoroborate is filtered, washed, and dried. In the above example the dry salt is heated in a flask set for distillation with a trap for the boron trifluoride. The fluoroborate decomposes, and the product distills at 75–87°.

A variety of experimental procedures for decomposing diazonium salts have given satisfactory results.[3] Diluents such as potassium chloride or bromide, ammonium chloride, barium sulfate, sodium fluoride, and sand have been employed. The optimum reaction conditions vary with the position and nature of substituents on the aromatic nucleus.

References

1. G. Balz and G. Schiemann, *Ber. deut. Chem. Ges.* **60,** 1186 (1927).
2. For a review of the Schiemann reaction, see A. Roe, *in* "Organic Reactions" (R. Adams, ed.), Vol. V, p. 193. Wiley, New York, 1949.
3. H. Schwechten, *Ber. deut. Chem. Ges.* **65,** 1605 (1932).

Schmidt Reaction

Karl Friedrich Schmidt (1887–   ) collaborated with Curtius at the University of Heidelberg on some research dealing with the action of sulfurylazide ($HN_3SO_2N_3H$) on p-xylene. He continued his work along similar lines at the Åbo Academy (Swedish University), Finland, in 1922. Schmidt's presentation of his work dealing with the action of hydrazoic acid on aldehydes and ketones was made at a meeting of the German Chemical Society at Jena in 1923. Later Schmidt returned to Heidelberg where he was appointed professor of chemistry. He has been particularly interested in the use of hydrazoic acid for the preparation of different types of organic compounds.

The conversion of a carboxylic acid into an amine by treatment with hydrazoic acid in concentrated sulfuric acid is called the Schmidt reaction.[1] Other carbonyl compounds besides acids are within the scope of the Schmidt reaction.[2] Aldehydes and ketones react with hydrazoic acid to give as main products nitriles and amides, respectively. The transformations are illustrated by the following equations.

$$RCOOH + HN_3 \longrightarrow RNH_2$$

$$RCHO + HN_3 \longrightarrow RCN$$

$$R_2CO + HN_3 \longrightarrow RCONHR$$

The reaction of benzaldehyde with hydrazoic acid gives a mixture of benzonitrile and formanilide.

$$C_6H_5CHO + HN_3 \longrightarrow C_6H_5CN + HCONHC_6H_5$$

The yields of the products vary with the molar ratio of the sulfuric acid employed.[3] The higher the ratio, the greater is the yield of formanilide.

Compounds sensitive to or sulfonated by concentrated sulfuric acid are not suited for the Schmidt reaction.[4] With malonic acids, under the condition of the Schmidt reaction, only one carboxyl group is converted to an amino group. The products are α-amino acids. Dicarboxylic acids, in which the two functions are separated by more than one methylene group, give diamino compounds.[5] Diamino acids, such as lysine and ornithine, have been prepared by this method.[6]

The mechanism of the Schmidt reaction was investigated by Newman and Gildenhorn.[7] Evidence is given for the formation of an oxocarbonium ion, R—$\overset{+}{C}$=O, from the reaction of 2,4,6-trimethylbenzoic acid with sulfuric acid. This ion (I) can react with hydrazoic acid, according to the proposed mechanism, to give an intermediate (II), which by a loss of nitrogen and migration of the R group with its pair of electrons yields the ion (III).

$$R-\overset{+}{C}O \ +:\overset{..}{N}H-\overset{+}{N}\equiv N: \longrightarrow R-CONH-\overset{+}{N}\equiv N: \longrightarrow [CO-\overset{..}{N}HR]^+ + N_2$$
$$\text{I} \qquad\qquad\qquad\qquad \text{II} \qquad\qquad\qquad\qquad \text{III}$$

The amine is formed from III by treatment with water. Migration of R proceeds with retention of configuration. This is also true for the Hofmann and Curtius reactions in which a similar migration of an R: group is involved.[4]

The successful use of polyphosphoric acid (PPA) in the Schmidt reaction with a variety of ketones has been reported by Conley.[8] This acid serves as a solvent as well as a dehydrating agent. Starting with cyclopentanone an 83% yield of piperidone was obtained by this procedure.

$$\underset{}{\bigcirc}=O \ + NaN_3 \ \xrightarrow[\text{PPA}]{55°, \ 9.5 \ \text{hrs.}} \ \underset{\underset{H}{N}}{\bigcirc}=O$$

Spiro[4.4]nonan-1-one on treatment with hydrazoic acid in polyphosphoric acid at 50° yields $\Delta^{8,9}$-hydrinden-4-one.[9] At lower temperatures and shorter reaction times an unsaturated nitrile was obtained.

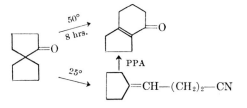

An investigation of the Schmidt reaction with unsymmetrical ketones has been reported by Smith and Horwitz.[10] Evidence is presented which indicates that a geometric pattern is involved similar to that observed in the Beckmann rearrangement.[11] The configuration of the intermediate (IV) will determine which R group migrates.

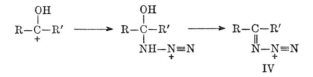

In the Schmidt reaction with some basically-substituted cyclic ketones it has been shown that the migrating group is predominately the one carrying the basic substituent.[12] This is explained by the orientation of the protonated basic center *anti* to the positively charged —$\overset{+}{N}\equiv N$ group. The electrostatic effect decreases as the nitrogen atom of the basic center is moved away from the reaction center.

References

1. K. F. Schmidt, Z. *angew. Chem.* **36**, 511 (1923).
2. A review of the Schmidt reaction is given by H. Wolff, *in* "Organic Reactions" (R. Adams, ed.), Vol. III, p. 307. Wiley, New York, 1946.
3. W. E. McEwen, W. E. Conrad, and C. A. VanderWerf, *J. Am. Chem. Soc.* **74**, 1168 (1952).
4. A comparison of the Curtius, Hofmann, and Schmidt reactions is given by P. A. S. Smith, *in* "Organic Reactions" (R. Adams, ed.), Vol. III, p. 363. Wiley, New York, 1946.
5. D. M. Hall, S. Mahboob, and E. E. Turner, *J. Chem. Soc.* p. 1842 (1950).
6. S. Rothchild and M. Fields, *J. Org. Chem.* **16**, 1080 (1951).
7. M. S. Newman and H. L. Gildenhorn, *J. Am. Chem. Soc.* **70**, 317 (1948).
8. R. T. Conley, *J. Org. Chem.* **23**, 1330 (1958).
9. R. T. Conley and B. E. Nowak, *Chem. & Ind.* (*London*) p. 1161 (1959).
10. P. A. S. Smith and J. P. Horwitz, *J. Am. Chem. Soc.* **72**, 3718 (1950).
11. G. M. Badger, R. T. Howard, and A. Simons, *J. Chem. Soc.* p. 2849 (1952).
12. H. J. Schwed, A. Hunger, and K. Hoffmann, *Helv. Chim. Acta* **33**, 607 (1958).

Skraup Reaction

Zdenko Hans Skraup (1850–1910) was born in Prague, Czechoslovakia. He began his active career in chemistry as an assistant to Rochleder and later to Lieben at the University of Vienna. With Rochleder, Skraup investigated the quinoline alkaloid, cinchonine. His work in this field helped elucidate the structure of this important alkaloid. In 1877, Prudhomme described the dye, alizarin blue, which is obtained by heating nitroalizarin with glycerin and sulfuric acid. In 1880, Graebe determined the structure of alizarin blue and showed that the reaction with glycerin results in the formation of a pyridine ring. From this work Skraup reasoned that quinoline should be produced when nitrobenzene reacts with glycerin and sulfuric acid. His work proved him to be correct. By including aniline in the reaction mixture a better procedure was obtained.

The preparation of quinoline and its derivatives by heating a primary aromatic amine with the corresponding nitro compound, glycerin, and concentrated sulfuric acid is known as the Skraup reaction. Skraup presented his new reaction in 1880.[1]

The nitro compound, which acts as an oxidizing agent, has been replaced for the most part by arsenic acid. The use of m-nitrobenzenesulfonic acid as the oxidizing agent has been reported to give very favorable results.[2,3] Boric acid has been used in the reaction mixture to moderate the initially vigorous reaction.

The mechanism of the Skraup reaction probably involves the formation of acrolein from glycerin.[4] The preparation and structure proof of 1,2-dihydroquinoline, an intermediate in the above sequence, has been described by Johnson and Buell.[5]

218

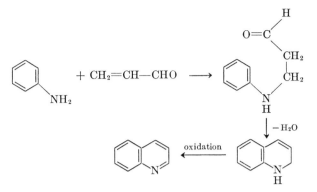

Although the reaction of aniline with acrolein fails to give a significant yield of quinoline, Yale,[6] in his modification of the Skraup reaction employing acrolein, was able to obtain respectable yields of substituted quinolines. The reaction was carried out in phosphoric acid (85%) at 100°. Compounds capable of yielding acrolein have also been employed in this modified procedure.

The reaction of several aromatic amines with glycerin in dilute sulfuric acid has been reported[2,3] to give satisfactory results. With 60–70% sulfuric acid the Skraup reaction proceeds without violence, and usually excellent yields are obtained. Bradford, et al.[3] have demonstrated that in the Skraup reaction with several *meta*-substituted anilines, the formation of 5- and 7-substituted quinolines is dependent upon the nature of the *meta* substituent. Strongly *ortho*- and *para*-directing groups produced only the 7-substituted quinoline. Weakly *ortho*- and *para*-directing groups gave a mixture in which the 7-substituted quinoline predominated, and *meta*-directing groups gave a mixture in which the 5-substituted quinoline derivative predominated.[7]

References

1. Z. H. Skraup, *Monatsh. Chem.* 1, 316 (1880); *Monatsh. Chem.* 2, 139 (1881).
2. British Patent 394,416 (1933).
3. L. Bradford, T. J. Elliott, and F. M. Rowe, *J. Chem. Soc.* p. 437 (1947).
4. For a discussion of the Skraup reaction, see F. W. Bergstrom, *Chem. Revs.* 35, 152–153 (1944).
5. W. S. Johnson and B. G. Buell, *J. Am. Chem. Soc.* 74, 4517 (1952).
6. H. L. Yale and J. Bernstein, *J. Am. Chem. Soc.* 70, 254 (1948).
7. A review of the Skraup synthesis of quinolines is given by R. H. F. Manske and M. Kulka, *in* "Organic Reactions" (R. Adams, ed.), Vol. VII, p. 59. Wiley, New York, 1953.

Sommelet Reaction

Marcel Sommelet (1877–1952) was born at Langes, France, the son of a pharmacist. He studied at Paris and received his degree in pharmacy in 1902. He then worked under Béhal and received the Doctor of Science degree in 1906. After World War I, Sommelet joined the Faculté de Pharmacie at Paris and in 1934 succeeded Béhal in the chair of organic chemistry. His life was devoted to science.

Some of his contributions to organic chemistry include the preparation of aliphatic aldehydes from substituted hydroxyethyl ethyl ethers, the use of chloromethyl ethyl ether in the Grignard reaction, and the synthesis of benzyl chlorides. The latter were used in the preparation of benzyl alcohols and benzaldehydes (Sommelet reaction). Sommelet synthesized p-isopropylbenzaldehyde and showed its identity with natural cuminic aldehyde. He found that benzhydryltrimethylammonium hydroxide was converted by sulfuric acid to o-benzylbenzyldimethylamine (*Sommelet rearrangement*).

For his outstanding work, Sommelet shared the Jecker Prize with E. Fourneau and L. Maillard in 1919, and more recently received the Jungfleish Prize.

In 1913, Sommelet[1] discovered that the quaternary salts prepared from benzyl halides and hexamethylenetetramine are decomposed by heating in the presence of water to give the corresponding aryl aldehyde. The reaction is general for the synthesis of aromatic aldehydes and usually gives satisfactory yields. It can be represented by the following equation:

$$\text{ArCH}_2\text{X} \longrightarrow [\text{ArCH}_2 \cdot \text{C}_6\text{H}_{12}\text{N}_4]^+\text{X}^- \longrightarrow \text{ArCHO}$$

Other products isolated from this reaction were ammonia, methyl-, dimethyl-, and trimethylamine, as well as some benzylamine. Sommelet found that isolation of the quaternary salt is unnecessary. By simply heating benzyl chloride with hexamethylenetetramine in aqueous-alcohol solution, benzaldehyde is formed in good yield.

The reaction was investigated by Angyal and coworkers.[2-4] They showed that electron-attracting substituents on the aromatic ring decrease the rate and yield in the Sommelet reaction. According to these authors the best solvent for the reaction is 50% acetic acid. Their study indicated that the mechanism of the reaction first involves the hydrolysis of the quaternary salt to form the arylmethylamine. The latter undergoes dehydrogenation to the imine, which on hydrolysis gives the aldehyde.[5]

$$ArCH_2NH_2 \longrightarrow ArCH{=}NH \longrightarrow ArCHO$$

The hexamethylenetetramine hydrolysis product, $CH_2{=}NH$, is probably the hydrogen acceptor in the conversion of the amine to the imine. This would account for the formation of methylamine. According to Shopee[6] the thermodynamic evidence supports this mechanism. The dehydrogenating action of hexamethylenetetramine (I) has been demonstrated by Duff[7] in the formation of Schiff bases from bis(o-hydroxybenzyl)amines.

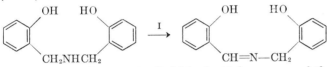

The preparation of aromatic dialdehydes[4,8] by means of the Sommelet reaction is satisfactory for the m- and p-bis(chloromethyl) compounds provided that at least one position ortho to the chloromethyl group is unsubstituted. The o-bis(chloromethyl) derivatives yielded basic nitrogen compounds upon hydrolysis of the hexamethylenetetramine salts.[8]

Hass and Bender[9] have described a general method for the preparation of substituted benzaldehydes which is comparable to the Sommelet reaction. By treatment of a benzyl halide, e.g., o-xylyl bromide, with the sodium salt of 2-nitropropane in alcohol, o-tolualdehyde is obtained in about 70% yield.[10]

$$\text{(CH}_3\text{, CH}_2\text{Br-benzene)} + Na^+[(CH_3)_2C{=}NO_2]^- \longrightarrow$$

$$\text{(CH}_3\text{, CHO-benzene)} + (CH_3)_2C{=}NOH + NaBr$$

Terephthaldehyde has been prepared in 80% yield by the *Haas and Bender procedure* from the reaction of α,α'-dibromo-p-xylene with alcoholic potassium hydroxide and 2-nitropropane.[11]

Another method of preparing aldehydes from benzyl halides is the *Kröhnke reaction*.[12] This involves the preparation of a pyridinium salt which is allowed to react with p-nitrosodimethylaniline (II) to give a nitrone. Acid hydrolysis of this intermediate yields the aldehyde and p-dimethylaminophenylhydroxylamine.

$$ArCH_2X + C_5H_5N \longrightarrow [ArCH_2\overset{+}{N}C_5H_5]X^- \overset{II}{\longrightarrow}$$

$$ArCH{=}N{-}\!\!\left\langle\bigcirc\right\rangle\!\!-N(CH_3)_2 \overset{H_3O^+}{\longrightarrow} ArCHO + (CH_3)_2N{-}\!\!\left\langle\bigcirc\right\rangle\!\!-NHOH$$
$$\overset{\downarrow}{O}$$

The reaction has wide application. Good yields of aromatic, unsaturated, and α-keto aldehydes can be obtained under mild conditions.

Active methyl groups in heterocyclic systems react with iodine and pyridine to form pyridinium iodides which were converted to aldehydes by the Kröhnke procedure.[13] In this way 2-benzothiazolecarboxaldehyde was prepared in 84% yield from the corresponding 2-methylbenzothiazole.

References

1. M. Sommelet, *Compt. rend. acad. sci.* **157**, 852 (1913).
2. S. J. Angyal and R. C. Rassack, *Nature* **161**, 723 (1948).
3. S. J. Angyal and R. C. Rassack, *J. Chem. Soc.* p. 2700 (1949).
4. S. J. Angyal, P. J. Morris, R. C. Rassack, and J. A. Waterer, *J. Chem. Soc.* p. 2704 (1949); a review of the Sommelet reaction is given by S. J. Angyal *in* "Organic Reactions" (R. Adams, ed.), Vol. VIII, p. 197. Wiley, New York, 1954.
5. The mechanism has been investigated with $PhCD_2NH_2$ by V. Franzen, *Ann. Chem. Liebigs* **600**, 109 (1956).
6. C. W. Shopee, *Nature* **162**, 619 (1948).
7. J. C. Duff and V. I. Furness, *J. Chem. Soc.* p. 1512 (1951); see Duff reaction, p. 84.
8. J. H. Wood, C. C. Tung, M. A. Perry, and R. E. Gibson, *J. Am. Chem. Soc.* **72**, 2992 (1950).
9. H. B. Hass and M. L. Bender, *J. Am. Chem. Soc.* **71**, 1767 (1949).
10. H. B. Hass and M. L. Bender, *in* "Organic Syntheses" (A. C. Cope, ed.), Vol. 30, p. 99. Wiley, New York, 1950.
11. A. R. Surrey and J. R. Mayer, *J. Med. Pharm. Chem.* In press.
12. F. Kröhnke and E. Börner, *Ber. deut. Chem. Ges.* **69**, 2006 (1936).
13. W. Reid and H. Bender, *Chem. Ber.* **89**, 1893 (1956).

Stephen Reaction

Henry Stephen studied at Victoria University, Manchester, where he received the Doctor of Science degree in 1920. He served on the faculty at Victoria University and became a senior lecturer in 1921. Since 1926, Stephen has been professor of chemistry and chemical engineering at the University of the Witwatersrand, Johannesburg, South Africa.

At Manchester Stephen collaborated with Chaim Weizmann, who became president of the State of Israel in 1949. Their research included condensations involving cyanoacetic, malonic, and acetoacetic esters.

The Stephen reaction consists in the conversion of an aliphatic or aromatic nitrile to the corresponding aldehyde by treatment with hydrogen chloride and anhydrous stannous chloride in absolute ether.[1] The reaction, which is illustrated by the following sequence, is usually carried out by adding the nitrile to anhydrous stannous chloride dissolved in ether with dry hydrogen chloride. In most cases the iminohydrochloride stannic chloride complex can be isolated and hydrolyzed to the aldehyde by heating with water. The first step in the reaction probably involves formation of a nitrilium salt.

$$RCN \xrightarrow[\text{HCl}]{\text{SnCl}_2} [RC\equiv NH]_2SnCl_4 \longrightarrow [RCH\!=\!NH_2]_2SnCl_6 \xrightarrow{H_2O} RCHO$$

The conversions of 2-naphthonitrile to 2-naphthaldehyde[2] and of 4-methoxyphenylacetonitrile to 4-methoxyphenylacetaldehyde[3] are examples of the Stephen reaction.

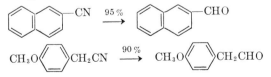

1-Naphthaldehyde cannot be prepared by this method.

Lieber[4] has shown that, in the reaction with lauronitrile, the aldimine complex can be precipitated by storing the ether solution at low temperatures. By reversing the usual procedure in the Stephen reaction, i.e., by adding stannous chloride to lauronitrile in ether saturated with hydrogen chloride, an ether-soluble liquid-type metallo complex can be isolated in quantitative yield. On boiling with water, the complex yields monomeric lauraldehyde.

According to Turner,[5] precipitation of the aldimine stannichloride appears to be the main factor which drives the reaction to completion. In unsubstituted aliphatic nitriles, structure has little effect on the rate of the reaction, whereas in substituted benzonitriles electron-repelling groups increase the rate considerably. Addition of acetyl chloride and water to hydrated stannous chloride in ether gives a homogeneous reaction mixture containing the anhydrous salt, acetic acid, and hydrogen chloride.

Stephen[6] has reported a modification of his reaction in which ethyl formate or ethyl acetate is used as a solvent in place of anhydrous ether. Anhydrous stannous chloride and nitriles are readily soluble in both solvents, and remain in solution after saturation with hydrogen chloride. The aldimine complex is purified, poured into water, and the aldehyde may be obtained by steam distillation.

The conversion of aliphatic and aromatic nitriles to the corresponding aldehydes in very good yields by means of lithium triethoxyaluminohydride has been reported recently by Brown and co-workers.[7]

The reduction of nitriles using Raney nickel catalyst in the presence of semicarbazide has also been used to prepare aldehydes.[8] By this method benzyl cyanide was converted to the semicarbazone of phenylacetaldehyde in 70% yield.

The Stephen reduction is related to the *Sonn and Müller reaction*[9,10] which involves the conversion of an anilide to an aldehyde. Treatment of the anilide with phosphorus pentachloride gives the imidyl chloride.

$$\text{R—CONHAr} \xrightarrow{\text{PCl}_5} \text{R—}\overset{\text{Cl}}{\underset{|}{\text{C}}}\text{=NAr} \xrightarrow{\text{SnCl}_2} \text{R—}\overset{\text{H}}{\underset{|}{\text{C}}}\text{=NAr} \xrightarrow[\text{H}^+]{\text{H}_2\text{O}} \text{RCHO}$$

Reduction with stannous chloride in ether replaces the chlorine atom by hydrogen. A salt of the Schiff base is probably formed which on heating with dilute acid or water decomposes to give the aldehyde.

By this method *o*-toluanilide is converted to *o*-tolualdehyde in 70% yield.[11]

References

1. H. Stephen, *J. Chem. Soc.* **127**, 1874 (1925).
2. J. W. Williams, *in* "Organic Syntheses" (L. I. Smith, ed.), Vol. 23, p. 63. Wiley, New York, 1943.
3. W. C. Evans and N. Walker, *J. Chem. Soc.* p. 1571 (1947).
4. E. Lieber, *J. Am. Chem. Soc.* **71**, 2862 (1949).
5. L. Turner, *J. Chem. Soc.* p. 1686 (1956).
6. T. Stephen and H. Stephen, *J. Chem. Soc.* p. 4695 (1956).
7. H. C. Brown, C. J. Shoaf, and C. P. Garg, *Tetrahedron Letters No. 3*, 9 (1959).
8. H. Plieninger and G. Werst, *Angew. Chem.* **67**, 156 (1955).
9. A. Sonn and E. Müller, *Ber. deut. Chem. Ges.* **52**, 1927 (1919).
10. The Stephen and Sonn and Müller reactions are included in a review of syntheses of aldehydes from carboxylic acids, by E. Mossetig, *in* "Organic Reactions" (R. Adams, ed.), Vol. VIII, p. 218. Wiley, New York, 1954.
11. J. W. Williams, C. H. Witten, and J. A. Krynitsky, *in* "Organic Syntheses" (H. Adkins, ed.), Vol. 26, p. 97. Wiley, New York, 1946.

Stevens Rearrangement

In 1928 Stevens showed that, when an aqueous solution of phenacylbenzyldimethylammonium bromide (I) was treated with sodium amalgam or heated with dilute sodium hydroxide solution, a rearrangement of a benzyl group occurred, to give the acetophenone derivative (II).[1]

$$C_6H_5COCH_2\overset{\overset{\displaystyle H_3C}{|}}{\underset{\underset{\displaystyle CH_3}{|}}{N^+}}-CH_2C_6H_5 \quad \overset{OH^-}{\longrightarrow} \quad C_6H_5COCH-N(CH_3)_2$$

I   II

Electronegative substituents on the benzene nucleus of the phenacyl group retard the shift of a benzyl group from the nitrogen atom to the adjacent carbon atom, whereas their presence in the benzyl group accelerates the reaction.[2,3]

Brewster and Kline[4] have investigated the stereochemistry of the Stevens rearrangement and have confirmed the view of Stevens that

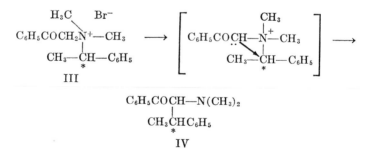

an intramolecular migration is involved. These workers showed that the rearrangement of *l*-phenacyl-α-phenylethyldimethylammonium bromide (III) to the amino ketone (IV) proceeds with little racemization.

References

1. T. S. Stevens, E. M. Creighton, A. B. Gordon, and M. MacNicol, *J. Chem. Soc.* p. 3193 (1928).
2. J. L. Dunn and T. S. Stevens, *J. Chem. Soc.* p. 1926 (1932).
3. See also C. R. Hauser and S. W. Kantor, *J. Am. Chem. Soc.* 73, 1437 (1951).
4. J. H. Brewster and M. W. Kline, *J. Am. Chem. Soc.* 74, 5179 (1952).

Stobbe Condensation

Hans Stobbe (1860–1938) was born in Tiegenhof, Germany. He studied at Heidelberg, Munich, Strassburg, and Leipzig, where he received his doctor's degree (1889) under Wislicenus. He joined the faculty there and became professor of chemistry in 1894.

His work on the preparation of teraconic acid from acetone and diethyl succinate led to a general investigation of carbonyl compounds with succinic esters (Stobbe condensation). In connection with his interest in photochemical problems, Stobbe synthesized about 60 fulgides, dialkylidenesuccinic acid anhydrides. Stobbe also studied the polymerization of styrene by light and heat. This work laid the foundation for polymer chemistry.

Stobbe was an editor of Poggendorff's "Biographisch-Literarisches Handwörterbuch."

The condensation of aldehydes and ketones with succinic esters in the presence of a basic catalyst to give alkylidenesuccinic acids is referred to as the Stobbe condensation.[1] An example is the reaction of acetone, diethyl succinate, and sodium ethoxide to form teraconic acid.[2]

$$\begin{array}{c}H_3C \\ \diagdown \\ C{=}O \\ \diagup \\ H_3C\end{array} + \begin{array}{c}CH_2{-}COOC_2H_5 \\ | \\ CH_2{-}COOC_2H_5\end{array} \xrightarrow[\text{2. H}^+]{\text{1. NaOC}_2\text{H}_5} \begin{array}{c}H_3C \qquad CH_2{-}COOH \\ \diagdown \qquad | \\ C{=}C{-}COOH \\ \diagup \\ H_3C\end{array}$$

The usual procedure is to allow the reaction mixture to stand in the cold for several days or weeks. Addition of water followed by acidification affords the half-ester which can be hydrolyzed with barium or

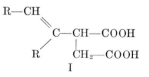

$$\begin{array}{c}R{-}CH \\ \diagdown\diagdown \\ C{-}CH{-}COOH \\ \diagup \qquad | \\ R \qquad CH_2{-}COOH \\ \text{I}\end{array}$$

sodium hydroxide to the diacid. If the ketone has an α-hydrogen, the product may contain the tautomeric alkenylsuccinic acid (I), which in certain cases is the exclusive product.

A side reaction encountered in the Stobbe condensation is the reduction of some ketone to the corresponding alcohol. This can be eliminated by the use of *tert*-butoxide in *tert*-butyl alcohol with dimethyl succinate. Under these conditions the yields are usually better and the reaction times shorter than with sodium ethoxide. The condensation of benzophenone with diethyl succinate in the presence of potassium *tert*-butoxide gives a 94% yield of β-carbethoxy-γ,γ-diphenylvinylacetic acid (II).[3] The reaction time is thirty minutes.

$$CH_2-COOH$$
$$(C_6H_5)_2C=C-COOC_2H_5$$
$$II$$

The condensation of diethyl phenylsuccinate with cycloheptanone in the presence of potassium *tert*-butoxide gives the half-ester β-carbethoxy-β-(cyclohepten-1-yl)-α-phenylpropionic acid.[4] The double bond is pictured in the endocyclic position. The successful application of the Stobbe reaction to ethyl β-aroylpropionates (ArCOCH₂CH₂-COOC₂H₅) has been reported using sodium hydride as the catalyst.[5]

The Stobbe condensation has a wide scope. A large variety of carbonyl compounds including aliphatic and aromatic aldehydes and ketones have been employed. Some of the products obtained via the Stobbe condensation include lactones, naphthols, indones, tetralones, and fulgides.

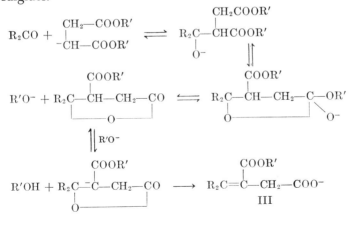

The mechanism of the Stobbe condensation probably involves an intermediary paraconic ester. This would account for the specificity of a succinic ester in the reaction. The primary product is always the half-ester (III), which is frequently isolated in high yield.

References

1. For a review of the Stobbe condensation, see W. S. Johnson and G. H. Daub, in "Organic Reactions" (R. Adams, ed.), Vol. VI, p. 1. Wiley, New York, 1951.
2. H. Stobbe, *Ber. deut. Chem. Ges.* **26**, 2312 (1895).
3. W. S. Johnson and W. P. Schneider, in "Organic Syntheses" (A. C. Cope, ed.), Vol. 30, p. 18. Wiley, New York, 1950.
4. A. M. Islam and M. T. Zemaity, *J. Am. Chem. Soc.* **80**, 5806 (1958).
5. E. D. Bergmann, S. Yaroslavsky, and H. Weiler-Feilchefeld, *J. Am. Chem. Soc.* **81**, 2775 (1959).

Stork Reaction

Gilbert J. Stork (1921–   ) was born in Brussels, Belgium. He received the B.S. degree in 1942 from the University of Florida, and his doctorate in 1945 from the University of Wisconsin under Professor McElvain. After teaching at Harvard University, Stork went to Columbia University (1953) where he is now professor of chemistry. His main interests in chemistry include the design of symbolic reactions, synthesis of natural products, and reaction mechanisms.

Stork has received many honors including the American Chemical Society Award in Pure Chemistry in 1957. He is an honorary editor of *Tetrahedron* and associate editor of the *Journal of Organic Chemistry*.

The C-alkylation and acylation of carbonyl compounds via the preparation of an enamine intermediate has become known as the Stork reaction.[1,2] As commonly applied, an aldehyde or ketone reacts with pyrrolidine in the presence of a catalytic quantity of *p*-toluenesulfonic acid to give the enamine which then may be alkylated or acylated to give the corresponding substituted carbonyl derivative. To date, the Stork reaction has been most useful for C-acylations and Michael additions.

An example of considerable interest is the preparation of ethyl 2-oxo-cyclohexaneacetate (II) from cyclohexanone and ethyl bromoacetate:[1,3,4]

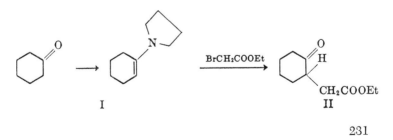

BrCH₂COOEt

I   II

Similarly the enamine I may be alkylated with methyl iodide to give 2-methylcyclohexanone in 70% yield.[2] The early studies in enamine formation[5] indicated that the reaction was general and could be reversed readily. It therefore became useful as a protecting group, as for example, in the case of 3-keto steroids.

Enamines have been used for the preparation of tetrahydrocinnolines,[4] in the synthesis of *dl*-protolichesterinic acid,[6] in synthetic studies relating to colchicine,[7] and recently in the introduction of an α-fluorine atom in steroids:[8]

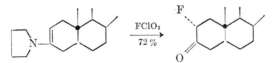

In a study of alicyclic ketones, it has been shown that the enamine intermediate may be alkylated readily with cyanogen chloride, acrylonitrile, or methyl acrylate.[2] For example, cyclopentanone pyrrolidine enamine which is prepared in 75% yield, reacts with cyanogen chloride to give 2-cyanocyclopentanone in 46% yield.[3]

An extremely interesting variation of the Stork reaction involves the reaction of methyl vinyl ketone with the enamine prepared from cyclohexanone to give Δ[1,9]-2-octalone (III).[2]

The nucleophilic character of the enamine intermediate is apparent when one considers the resonance involved:

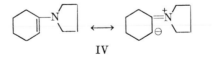

With cyanogen chloride, C-alkylation could be pictured as a nucleophilic attack by IV on this reagent to give the immonium salt V which loses a proton to give the new enamine VI. Hydrolysis would give the cyano ketone VII.

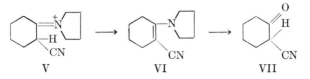

V   VI   VII

References

1. G. Stork, R. Terrell, and J. Szmuskovicz, *J. Am. Chem. Soc.* **76**, 2029 (1954).
2. G. Stork and H. K. Landsman, *J. Am. Chem. Soc.* **78**, 5128 (1956).
3. M. E. Kuehne, *J. Am. Chem. Soc.* **81**, 5400 (1959).
4. H. E. Baumgarten, P. L. Creger, and C. E. Villars, *J. Am. Chem. Soc.* **80**, 6609 (1958).
5. C. Mannich and H. Davidsen, *Ber. deut. Chem. Ges.* **69B**, 2106 (1936); F. W. Heyl and M. E. Herr, *J. Am. Chem. Soc.* **75**, 1918 (1953); M. E. Herr and F. W. Heyl, *J. Am. Chem. Soc.* **74**, 3627 (1952).
6. E. E. van Tamelin and S. R. Bach, *J. Am. Chem. Soc.* **80**, 3079 (1958).
7. T. A. Crabb and K. Schofield, *J. Chem. Soc.* p. 4276 (1958).
8. R. B. Gabbard and E. V. Jensen, *J. Org. Chem.* **23**, 1406 (1958).

Ullmann Reaction

Fritz Ullmann (1875–1939) was born in Fürth, Bavaria. He studied under Graebe at the University of Geneva, where he became an assistant professor. From 1905 to 1925, Ullmann taught at the Technische Hochschule in Berlin and then returned to Geneva. His "Enzyklopaedie der technischen Chemie" is well known to organic chemists. Ullmann was interested in the synthesis of biphenyl and acridine derivatives. He synthesized some diaminoacridines which he gave to his friend, Paul Ehrlich, for chemotherapeutic evaluation. With Graebe, Ullmann synthesized carbazole.

When a halogenated aromatic compound is treated with copper at elevated temperatures, a biaryl molecule is formed. This reaction is known as the Ullmann reaction.[1,2] It is applicable to the synthesis of symmetrical and unsymmetrical biaryls and polyaryls. An example is the synthesis of biphenyl in 82% yield from iodobenzene.

$$2 \langle \rangle\!\!-\!\!I \xrightarrow{\text{Cu}} \langle \rangle\!\!-\!\!\langle \rangle + CuI_2$$

Iodo and activated chloro and bromo aromatic compounds have been successfully employed in this reaction. Electronegative groups in the *ortho* or *para* positions with respect to the halogen atom favor the Ullmann reaction. The usual procedure is to add an excess of the copper catalyst portionwise to the aromatic halide at a suitable temperature.

In some instances a solvent has been employed to moderate the reaction. Kornblum and Kendall[3] have shown that the use of dimethylformamide as a solvent for the Ullmann reaction results in higher yields than those obtained previously. For example, 2,2'-dinitrobiphenyl was obtained in 80% yield from *o*-chloronitrobenzene, as compared with previous yields of 52–61%.

234

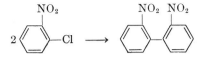

The same product has been prepared in practically quantitative yield by adding four equivalents of freshly precipitated copper (procedure given) to *o*-iodonitrobenzene at 190°.[4]

Evidence for a free-radical mechanism for the Ullmann reaction has been reported by Nursten.[5] The reaction with *p*-iodonitrobenzene was carried out in the presence of an antioxidant. With catechol the yield of dehalogenated product, nitrobenzene, was greater than that with resorcinol. Since the former is a better antioxidant the results point to a homolytic reaction.

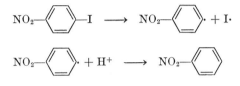

References

1. F. Ullmann, *Ber. deut. Chem. Ges.* **29**, 1878 (1896); *Ann. Chem. Liebigs* **332**, 38 (1904).
2. For a review of the Ullmann reaction, see P. E. Fanta, *Chem. Revs.* **38**, 139 (1946).
3. N. Kornblum and D. L. Kendall, *J. Am. Chem. Soc.* **74**, 5782 (1952).
4. P. H. Gore and G. K. Hughes, *J. Chem. Soc.* p. 1615 (1959).
5. H. E. Nursten, *J. Chem. Soc.* p. 3081 (1955).

Ullmann Condensation

Ullmann showed that the chlorine atom in *o*-chlorobenzoic acid would react with phenols, thiophenols, aryl sulfinic acids, and arylamines in the presence of catalytic amounts of copper.[1]

A large number of N-phenylanthranilic acid derivatives[2] synthesized by this method have been used as intermediates in the synthesis of 9-chloroacridines. The latter have been employed in the preparation of a variety of chemotherapeutic agents. The formation of N-(4-methoxyphenyl)-4-chloroanthranilic acid from 2,4-dichlorobenzoic acid and *p*-anisidine followed by cyclization with phosphorus oxychloride leads to 6,9-dichloro-2-methoxyacridine.

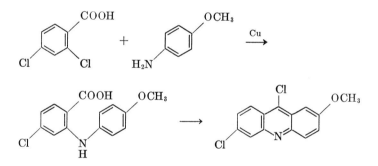

The Ullmann condensation is commonly carried out by heating the reactants in a solvent (amyl alcohol, isopropyl alcohol, glycerin) with anhydrous potassium carbonate and copper powder.

A discussion of the effects of substituents on the reactivity of the chlorobenzoic acid and aniline is given by Dauben.[3] An electronegative group *ortho* or *para* to the chlorine atom increases the positive charge at the carbon atom to which the chlorine atom is attached and thereby increases its activity. The reactivity of the nitrogen atom is

dependent upon the basic strength of the amine. A negative substituent on the arylamine nucleus inhibits the reaction.

The mechanism of the Ullmann condensation probably involves a
nucleophilic attack of the nitrogen atom on the carbon atom to which
the *ortho* chlorine is attached.

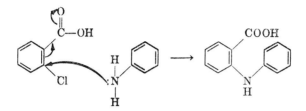

Another method of preparing substituted N-phenylanthranilic acids
is by the *Chapman rearrangement*,[4] which involves heating an imido
ester and hydrolyzing the product. For example, when the imido ester
(I) prepared from the sodium salt of methyl 2-chloro-6-hydroxy-
benzoate and N-4-methoxyphenylbenzimidyl chloride was heated at
210° for seventy minutes and the product saponified, the anthranilic
acid derivative (II) was obtained.[5]

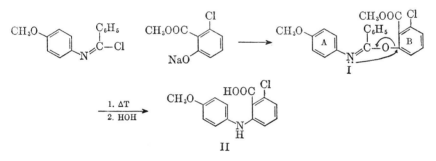

The rearrangement, which may be pictured as in the imido ester
(I), is similar to that suggested for the Ullmann condensation. Elec-
tropositive groups *ortho* or *para* to the nitrogen atom in ring A and
electronegative substituents in similar positions with respect to the
oxygen atom in ring B facilitate the rearrangement.[6]

The mechanism of the *Chapman rearrangement* has been investigated by Wiberg and Rowland.[7] The data obtained supports the four-
membered cyclic mechanism involving a nucleophilic displacement on
an aromatic ring.

References

1. F. Ullmann, *Ber. deut. Chem. Ges.* **36**, 2382 (1903); **37**, 2001 (1904); F. Ullmann and H. Kipper, *Ber. deut. Chem. Ges.* **38**, 2120 (1905).
2. See, for example, A. A. Goldberg and W. Kelly, *J. Chem. Soc.* p. 102 (1946).
3. W. G. Dauben, *J. Am. Chem. Soc.* **70**, 2420 (1948).
4. A. W. Chapman, *J. Chem. Soc.* **127**, 1992 (1925).
5. W. G. Dauben and R. L. Hodgson, *J. Am. Chem. Soc.* **72**, 3479 (1950).
6. G. Singh, S. Singh, A. Singh, and W. Singh, *J. Indian Chem. Soc.* **28**, 459 (1951).
7. K. B. Wiberg and B. I. Rowland, *J. Am. Chem. Soc.* **77**, 2205 (1955).

Wallach Reaction

Otto Wallach (1847–1931) was born in Königsberg, Prussia. He studied chemistry at Göttingen under Wöhler and at Berlin under Hofmann. In 1869, he received his doctor's degree at Göttingen and the following year became an assistant at Bonn, where he worked with Kekulé. In 1879, while Wallach was teaching pharmacy, he became interested in terpene chemistry. He succeeded Victor Meyer at Göttingen (1889), where he became director of the Chemical Institute. He retired in 1915.

Wallach's systematic investigations and classification of the terpenes brought order to this confused field of chemistry. His book "Terpene und Kampfer" served as the foundation for future work in this field. Wallach was also interested in azo and diazo compounds. In 1910, he was awarded the Nobel Prize in chemistry.

The reductive amination of an aldehyde or ketone with a primary or secondary amine and formic acid is called the Wallach reaction.[1] The process is closely related to the Leuckart reaction[2] and is sometimes referred to as the Leuckart-Wallach reaction. It can be illustrated by the general equation:

$$\underset{R'}{\overset{R}{>}}C=O + HN\underset{R'''}{\overset{R''}{<}} + HCOOH \longrightarrow \underset{R'}{\overset{R}{>}}CH-N\underset{R'''}{\overset{R''}{<}} + H_2O + CO_2$$

A study of the Wallach reaction is the subject of a publication by Staple and Wagner.[3] These authors showed that the formyl derivative of the amine is usually not involved in the Wallach reaction. Its formation impedes the reaction so that an excess of formic acid is not desirable. It is suggested that an initial condensation product is formed from the reaction of the carbonyl compound and the amine. This product, an hydroxyalkylamine, alkylidenediamine, or Schiff base, is reduced by formic acid. Treatment of 1,1'-benzylidenedipiperidine with formic acid gives a quantitative yield of 1-benzylpiperidine.

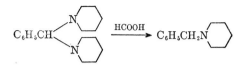

De Benneville and Macartney[4] have investigated the behavior of aliphatic aldehydes in the Wallach reaction. They were able to obtain good yields of alkylated amines both by direct reaction of the amine, formic acid, and aldehyde, and by enamine formation followed by reduction with formic acid. An example of the latter is the reaction of butyraldehyde and morpholine. The enamine formed from the diimine by distillation can be isolated and reduced to the amine by means of formic acid.

$$C_3H_7CHO + 2NHR_2 \xrightarrow[\text{catalyst}]{5-50°} C_3H_7CH(NR_2)_2 \xrightarrow{\Delta T}$$

$$CH_3CH_2CH{=}CHNR_2 \xrightarrow{HCOOH} CH_3CH_2CH_2CH_2NR_2$$

On the basis of this work, it was suggested that an enamine intermediate may be involved in the Wallach reaction.

References

1. O. Wallach, *Ann. Chem. Liebigs* **343**, 54 (1905).
2. See p. 157.
3. E. Staple and E. C. Wagner, *J. Org. Chem.* **14**, 559 (1949).
4. P. L. de Benneville and J. H. Macartney, *J. Am. Chem. Soc.* **72**, 3073 (1950).

Willgerodt Reaction

Conrad Willgerodt (1841–1930) was born in Harlingerode, Germany, the son of a farmer. He was graduated from a teacher's college in 1863. After some teaching he went to the Technical Institute at Braunschweig to study natural science and zoology. From there Willgerodt went to Berlin, where he attended the lectures by Hofmann. Two years later (1869) he was employed as a chemist in a dye company in Elberfeld. When he had accumulated sufficient money, Willgerodt continued his studies at Freiburg, where, within one year, he obtained his doctorate under Claus. His thesis was on a study of alizarin and hydroxyanthraquinone. At Freiburg, he became an associate professor in 1881 and a full professor in 1895. He taught for 37 years.

His main interest was in the chemistry of aromatic compounds. Some of his accomplishments include the halogenation of aromatic hydrocarbons in the presence of metals; the discovery (1886) of iodobenzene dichloride, the first organic compound containing trivalent iodine; and the formation of iodosobenzene from the dichloride. Willgerodt published a book on trivalent iodine.

The conversion of ketones to amides having the same number of carbon atoms by heating with aqueous ammonium polysulfide is known as the Willgerodt reaction.[1] An illustration is the formation of phenylacetamide from acetophenone. A small amount of ammonium phenylacetate is obtained in the reaction.

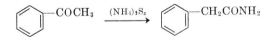

The reaction is also applicable to higher alkyl aryl ketones,[2] olefins, and acetylenes, as well as some aliphatic ketones and aldehydes.

$$ArCO(CH_2)_nCH_3 \longrightarrow Ar(CH_2)_{n+1}CONH_2$$

$$ArCH{=}CH_2 \longrightarrow ArCH_2CONH_2$$

$$ArC{\equiv}CH \longrightarrow ArCH_2CONH_2$$

It has been found that sulfur and a dry amine can be used in place of aqueous ammonium polysulfide. This is the Kindler[3] modification of the Willgerodt reaction, in which the product is the thioamide. For example, with morpholine,[4] the reaction with acetophenone gives the morpholine thioamide.

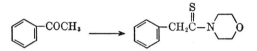

The mechanism of the Willgerodt reaction has been the subject of considerable discussion. It is generally accepted that there is a fundamental mechanism which involves an intermediate having an unsaturated side chain,[5] with progression of the unsaturated bond to the terminal methyl group.

$$ArCOCH_2CH_3 \rightleftharpoons ArCH{=}CHCH_3 \rightleftharpoons ArCH_2CH{=}CH_2$$

King and McMillan[6] have proposed a mechanism for the shifting of the unsaturated bond involving the addition and elimination of hydrogen sulfide with the formation of a primary thiol at the terminal carbon atom. These authors[7] have also investigated the mechanism for the conversion of the mercaptan to a carboxylic acid derivative.

$$RCOCH_3 \longrightarrow RCH_2CH_2SH \longrightarrow RCH_2\overset{\overset{\displaystyle S}{\|}}{C}{-}NR_2'$$

The mechanism has been investigated[8] using acetophenone labeled in the carbonyl group with C^{14}. The results indicate that the major reaction, as has been accepted previously, does not involve a rearrangement of the carbon skeleton. By converting the product, phenyl acetamide, to benzylamine via the Hofmann reaction, radioactivity was retained.

$$C_6H_5\overset{14}{C}OCH_3 \longrightarrow C_6H_5\overset{14}{C}H_2CONH_2 \longrightarrow C_6H_5\overset{14}{C}H_2NH_2$$

Some recent applications of the Willgerodt reaction have been with heterocyclic compounds. α-Picoline and quinaldine react with sulfur in the presence of morpholine to yield the thiomorpholides which on hydrolysis give the corresponding carboxylic acids.[9] 3-Pyra-

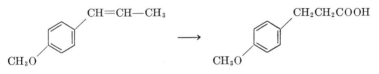

zolylacetic acids have been prepared from the corresponding 3-acetyl derivatives.[10]

The equivalence of $ArCOCH_2CH_3$ with $ArCH=CH-CH_3$ in the Willgerodt reaction is illustrated by the preparation of 3-anisylpro-pionic acid from anethole (4-propenylanisole).[9]

$$CH=CH-CH_3 \quad \longrightarrow \quad CH_2CH_2COOH$$

$$CH_3O \qquad\qquad\qquad\qquad CH_3O$$

References

1. C. Willgerodt, *Ber. deut. Chem. Ges.* **20**, 2467 (1887).
2. A review of the Willgerodt reaction is given by M. Carmack, *in* "Organic Reactions" (R. Adams, ed.), Vol. III, p. 83. Wiley, New York, 1946.
3. K. Kindler, *Arch. Pharm.* **265**, 389 (1927).
4. E. Schwenk and E. Bloch, *J. Am. Chem. Soc.* **64**, 3051 (1942).
5. M. Carmack and D. F. DeTar, *J. Am. Chem. Soc.* **68**, 2029 (1946).
6. J. A. King and F. H. McMillan, *J. Am. Chem. Soc.* **68**, 632 (1946).
7. F. H. McMillan and J. A. King, *J. Am. Chem. Soc.* **70**, 4143 (1948).
8. W. G. Dauben, J. C. Reid, P. E. Yankwich, and M. Calvin, *J. Am. Chem. Soc.* **72**, 121 (1950).
9. J. Schmitt and M. Suquet, *Bull. soc. chim. France* p. 755 (1956).
10. E. G. Brain and I. L. Finar, *J. Chem. Soc.* p. 2356 (1957).

Williamson Synthesis

Alexander William Williamson (1824–1904) was born in London, England. Poor health in childhood resulted in his loss of the use of one eye and one arm. Williamson studied chemistry at Heidelberg under Gmelin (1840) and then at Giessen (1844) under Liebig. In 1849 he was appointed professor at the University College in London, where his important work on the theory of etherification was carried out. This work offered experimental evidence for the empirical formulas of alcohols and ethers as proposed by Gerhart (1816–1856) and Laurent (1807–1853) which are accepted at the present time. Williamson was the first to prepare ortho esters. He received the Royal Medal in 1862.

A general method for the formation of ethers from the reaction of a metallic alkoxide with an alkyl halide is called the Williamson ether synthesis.[1] An illustration is the preparation of ethyl propyl ether from sodium propoxide and ethyl iodide.

$$C_3H_7ONa + C_2H_5I \longrightarrow C_2H_5OC_3H_7 + NaI$$

Another example is the synthesis of 4-chlorobutyl methyl ether from 1,4-dichlorobutane and sodium methoxide by refluxing in methanol for thirty hours.[2]

$$Cl(CH_2)_4Cl + NaOCH_3 \longrightarrow Cl(CH_2)_4OCH_3$$

By the proper selection of the reactants, both symmetrical and mixed ethers may be prepared. Usually no difficulty is encountered when primary halides and alcohols are used. For the preparation of secondary and tertiary alkyl ethers, the alcoholates of secondary and tertiary alcohols are employed. These are commonly prepared with potassium. The use of secondary and tertiary halides is unsatisfactory, since they can be converted to olefins with an alcoholate.

Phenols may also be used in the Williamson synthesis. The preparation of the plant hormone 2,4-dichlorophenoxyacetic acid is an example.

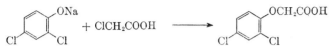

O-Alkylations are sometimes carried out with an alkyl halide and potassium carbonate in acetone. For example, the reaction of o-nitrophenol with n-butyl bromide gives n-butyl o-nitrophenyl ether in 80% yield.[3]

The preparation of alkyl iodides from the reaction of the corresponding chlorides or bromides with sodium iodide in acetone or methyl ethyl ketone has been designated as the *Finkelstein reaction.*[4]

$$RCl + NaI \xrightarrow{CH_3COC_2H_5} RI + NaCl$$

A novel method for the O-methylation of hydroxylic compounds was reported by Neeman *et al.*[5] Alcoholic hydroxyl groups can be methylated by diazomethane in the presence of catalytic amounts of fluoboric acid. Primary alcohols and unhindered secondary alcohols gave excellent yields of the methyl ether. α-Cholestanyl methyl ether was prepared by this method from α-cholestanol in 98% yield. The new reaction, which is particularly suitable for hydroxylic compounds sensitive to base, appears to occur directly at the alcoholic oxygen atom with retention of the original configuration of the carbinol.

References

1. A. W. Williamson, *J. Chem. Soc.* 4, 229 (1852).
2. R. C. Elderfield, B. M. Pitt, and I. Wempen, *J. Am. Chem. Soc.* 72, 1334 (1950).
3. C. F. H. Allen and J. W. Gates, *in* "Organic Syntheses" (W. E. Bachmann, ed.), Vol. 25, p. 9. Wiley, New York, 1945.
4. H. Finkelstein, *Ber. deut. Chem. Ges.* 43, 1528 (1910).
5. M. Neeman, M. C. Casiero, J. D. Roberts, and W. S. Johnson, *Tetrahedron* 6, 36 (1959).

Wittig Reaction

Georg Wittig (1897–   ) was born in Berlin, Germany. He received his doctor's degree at Marburg/Lahn under K. von Auwers. In 1932 he joined the faculty at the Technical Institute at Braunschweig and five years later went to the University of Freiburg. In 1949, he became professor and head of the chemistry department at Tübingen, and since 1956 has held a similar position at Heidelberg.

Wittig's main interests in chemistry include stereochemistry as well as radical and anionotropic reactions. He is a recipient of the Adolf von Baeyer Medal and has been elected to the Bavarian Academy of Sciences and the Heidelberger Academy of Sciences. In 1957, the Sorbonne awarded him an honorary doctor's degree.

The reaction of a triphenylphosphinealkylidene with a carbonyl compound to form an olefin, in which the carbonyl oxygen atom is replaced by a methylene group, has become known as the Wittig reaction.[1,2] The process involved is illustrated by the following example:

$$(C_6H_5)_3P + CH_3Br \longrightarrow [(C_6H_5)_3\overset{+}{P}CH_3]\overset{-}{B}r \xrightarrow{C_6H_5Li}$$

$$(C_6H_5)_3\overset{+}{P}—\overset{-}{C}H_2 + C_6H_6 + LiBr$$

$$(C_6H_5)_3\overset{+}{P}—\overset{-}{C}H_2 + (C_6H_5)_2CO \longrightarrow (C_6H_5)_2C{=}CH_2 + (C_6H_5)_3PO$$

Triphenylphosphine is allowed to react with methyl bromide to give triphenylmethylphosphonium bromide. Treatment of this salt with phenyllithium yields an alkylidenephosphine (ylid) which reacts with benzophenone to form 1,1-diphenylethylene and triphenylphosphine oxide. The latter can be reduced to regenerate triphenylphosphine.

A variety of bases have been used in the Wittig reaction. These include organolithium compounds, sodium amide, sodium methoxide,

246

and sodium carbonate. A recent modification is the use of lithium ethoxide[3] which gives good yields and simplifies the reaction.

Treatment of the phosphonium salt with a base may be carried out in ether, tetrahydrofuran, alcohol or water. The solution of the ylid is then treated with the carbonyl compound. Occasionally, the reverse addition is used, especially where the aldehyde or ketone contains an ester group.

The mechanism of the Wittig reaction has been described as follows:[4]

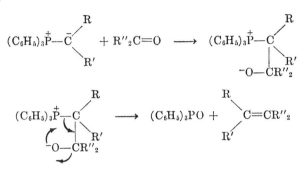

A wide variety of compounds, aliphatic and aromatic aldehydes, aliphatic, alicyclic, and aromatic ketones, formamides, isocyanates, ketenes, and nitroso compounds react with ylids to give the expected products. The use of chloromethyl ether to form the onium salt is the first step in a new synthesis of aldehydes.[5,6]

$$[(C_6H_5)_3\overset{+}{P}-CH_2OCH_3]Cl^- \longrightarrow (C_6H_5)_3P=CHOCH_3$$

$$(C_6H_5)_3P=CHOCH_3 + -\overset{|}{C}=O \longrightarrow -\overset{|}{C}=CHOCH_3$$

$$-\overset{|}{C}=CHOCH_3 \overset{H_3O^+}{\longrightarrow} -\overset{|}{C}HCHO$$

The reaction of fluorenone with an excess of triphenylphosphine-*n*-butylidene gives a cyclopropane derivative.[7]

The Wittig reaction has been applied in the synthesis of many natural products, including the cholesterol precursor, squalene, and lycopene, and the bixin esters. It offers a wide area of application.

References

1. G. Wittig and U. Schöllkopf, *Chem. Ber.* 87, 1318 (1954).
2. Reviews of the Wittig reaction are given by J. Levisalles, *Bull. soc. chim.*

France p. 1021 (1958); U. Schöllkopf, *Angew. Chem.* **71**, 260 (1959); S. Trippett *in* "Advances in Organic Chemistry" (R. A. Raphael, E. C. Taylor, and H. Wynberg, eds.), Vol. 1, pp. 83–102. Interscience, New York, 1960.
3. T. W. Campbell and R. N. McDonald, *J. Org. Chem.* **24**, 1246 (1959).
4. G. Wittig, *Angew. Chem.* **68**, 505 (1956).
5. S. G. Levine, *J. Am. Chem. Soc.* **80**, 6150 (1958).
6. G. Wittig and E. Knauss, *Angew. Chem.* **71**, 127 (1959).
7. R. Mechoulam and F. Sondheimer, *J. Am. Chem. Soc.* **80**, 4386 (1958).

248

Wohl-Ziegler Reaction

Alfred Wohl (1863–1939) was born in Graudenz, Germany. He studied at the University of Heidelberg and then at Berlin, where he received the Ph.D. degree in 1886 under A. W. Hofmann and later became an assistant professor. In 1904, he was appointed professor of chemistry at the Technische Hochschule in Danzig.

Wohl is probably best known for his method of degradation of aldose sugars.

* * *

Karl Ziegler (1898–   ) was born in Helsa near Cassel, Germany. He was a student of von Auwers at the University of Marburg, where he received the Ph.D. degree in 1920. After serving as an assistant and assistant professor at Marburg, Ziegler held a teaching position at the University of Frankfurt and then went to Heidelberg where he became head of the organic division. In 1936, Ziegler came to the United States as guest professor at the University of Chicago. He then returned to Germany to direct the chemistry department at Halle. In 1943, he was appointed director of the Max-Planck-Institut für Kohlenforschung at Mülheim/Ruhr.

Ziegler is noted for his work on organometallic compounds, free radicals, the synthesis of muscone and other polymethylene ketones, the synthesis of cantharidine, and the use of N-bromosuccinimide as a selective brominating agent.

Ziegler served as president of the German Chemical Society for several years. In 1959, he was elected honorary member of the Society of Chemistry and Industry.

A very useful method for selective bromination of many different types of compounds by means of a N-haloamide, particularly N-bromosuccinimide (NBS), is known as the Wohl-Ziegler reaction.[1,2] With olefins the allyl position and not the double bond is attacked.

For example, bromination of methyl crotonate with N-bromosuccinimide gives an 86% yield of methyl γ-bromocrotonate.

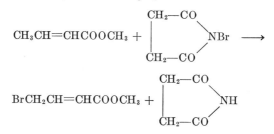

The reaction is usually carried out by refluxing the reactants in carbon tetrachloride until the N-bromosuccinimide is completely dissolved.

Another example of bromination in the allyl position is the formation of 7-bromocholesterol acetate from cholesterol acetate.[3]

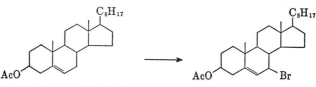

Removal of hydrogen bromide yields 7-dehydrocholesterol acetate, an intermediate in the synthesis of vitamin D_3.

The Wohl-Ziegler reaction has also been applied in the degradation of the bile acid side chain of steroids.[4] It was found that strong light is an effective catalyst in these reactions.

Nuclear brominations[5] have been successful with N-bromosuccinimide in the presence of metal chlorides ($AlCl_3$, $ZnCl_2$, and $FeCl_3$). An illustration is the preparation of p-bromotoluene from toluene.

The scope of the Wohl-Ziegler bromination was extended by Schmid and Karrer,[6] who found that dibenzoyl peroxide was an excellent catalyst in the reaction. With this catalyst, brominations of tertiary hydrogen atoms, conjugated dienes, and the side chain of toluene have been carried out. A 64% yield of benzyl bromide was obtained from toluene by this procedure.

Bromination of β-phenylpropionic acid with NBS gives a 58% yield of β-bromo-β-phenylpropionic acid indicating that the intermediate radical $C_6H_5\dot{C}HCH_2COOH$ is involved.[7] Since both methylene groups

$$C_6H_5CH_2CH_2COOH \xrightarrow{\text{NBS}} C_6H_5CHBrCH_2COOH$$

are available for attack it could therefore be concluded that the phenyl group has more stabilizing effect on the intermediate radical than a carboxyl group.

An extensive investigation of the allylic bromination of cyclohexene with NBS in carbon tetrachloride has been reported by Dauben and McCoy.[8] This general survey includes a study of the effect of environmental factors, impurities, added substances, and reaction times on the course of the reaction.

References

1. A. Wohl, *Ber. deut. Chem. Ges.* **52,** 51 (1919); K. Ziegler, A. Spaeth, E. Schaaf, W. Schumann, and E. Winkelmann, *Ann. Chem. Liebigs* **551,** 80 (1942).
2. A review of the Wohl-Ziegler reaction is given by C. Djerassi, *Chem. Revs.* **43,** 271 (1948).
3. A. E. Bide, H. B. Henhest, E. R. H. Jones, R. W. Peevers, and P. A. Wilkinson, *J. Chem. Soc.* p. 1783 (1948).
4. Miescher modification of the Barbier-Wieland degradation, see p. 7.
5. H. Schmid, *Helv. Chim. Acta* **29,** 1144 (1946).
6. H. Schmid and P. Karrer, *Helv. Chim. Acta* **29,** 573 (1946).
7. R. L. Huang and P. Williams, *J. Chem. Soc.* p. 2637 (1958).
8. H. J. Dauben and L. L. McCoy, *J. Am. Chem. Soc.* **81,** 4863 (1959).

Wolff-Kishner Reduction

Johann Ludwig Wolff (1857–1919) was born in Neustadt an der Haardt, Germany. He studied under Fittig at Strassburg, received the doctor's degree in 1882, and later became an instructor. In 1891, he joined the faculty as full professor in the analytical department at Jena, where Knorr was head of the department. Wolff was affiliated with Knorr at Jena for 27 years.

In addition to his work on the rearrangement of diazo ketones (Wolff rearrangement) and on the reduction of carbonyl compounds (Wolff-Kishner reduction), Wolff published work on the preparation of lactones, pyrazines, indoles from β-bromolevulinic acid and anilines, and tetronic acid derivatives. He discovered the first δ-lactone, the lactone from δ-hydroxycaproic acid.

By heating the hydrazone of a carbonyl compound in a sealed tube with sodium ethoxide or hydroxide as a catalyst, nitrogen is evolved and the corresponding methylene compound is formed. This method of reduction is known as the Wolff-Kishner reduction.[1]

$$\text{>CO} \xrightarrow{\text{N}_2\text{H}_4} \text{>C=N-NH}_2 \xrightarrow[\text{NaOC}_2\text{H}_5]{\text{NaOH or}} \text{>CH}_2 + \text{N}_2$$

The semicarbazone and azine derivatives have also been employed. In both cases, conversion to the hydrazone is essential before reduction occurs.

The method is suitable for the reduction of high-molecular weight carbonyl compounds as well as those sensitive to acid; the Clemmensen reduction (see p. 54), which is more generally employed for the reduction of aldehydes and ketones, is not satisfactory for these types of compounds. Furthermore, it has been shown with some α-amino ketones,[2] the expected product is obtained by the Wolff-Kishner reduction whereas anomalous products are formed via the Clemmensen method.

252

The reaction as originally carried out by Wolff[3] consists in heating the hydrazone with sodium ethoxide in a sealed tube at about 180° for several hours. There have been several modifications of the Wolff-Kishner method which make it possible to perform the reduction at atmospheric pressure and without isolation of the hydrazone. The use of glycols and high-boiling alcohols as the reaction medium with sodium as the catalyst has been reported.[4] Sodium methoxide in triethyleneglycol has also been employed.[5] The method using sodium or potassium hydroxide in diethylene or triethylene glycol as reported by Huang-Minlon[6] appears to be the most satisfactory modification of the Wolff-Kishner reduction. By this procedure, phenoxybenzoyl-propionic acid (I) was reduced in 95% yield to phenoxyphenylbutyric acid (II). Reduction of I via the Clemmensen method gave only a 54% yield of II.

The Huang-Minlon modification is applicable to large- as well as to small-scale reductions. In the Clemmensen method of reduction the yields fall off when the scale of operation is substantially greater than 50 grams. With aryl methyl ethers demethylation usually occurs in the Huang-Minlon modification. Oxidation of the resulting phenol is avoided by using an atmosphere of nitrogen and a shortened reaction period.[7] The reducing power of the reaction is increased considerably by using strictly anhydrous conditions.[8] Sterically-hindered carbonyl compounds may be reduced in this manner.

A study of the kinetics of the Wolff-Kishner reaction has been reported.[9] The mechanism of the reaction is believed to involve the formation of an anion followed by a shift of hydrogen with simultaneous loss of nitrogen to give a carbanion.

$$R_2C{=}N{-}NH_2 + B \rightleftharpoons R_2C{=}N{-}\bar{N}H + BH^+$$

$$R_2C{=}N{-}\bar{N}H \longrightarrow R_2\bar{C}H + N_2$$

$$R_2\bar{C}H + BH^+ \longrightarrow R_2CH_2 + B$$

A radical mechanism has been suggested for the reduction of fluorenone by the Wolff-Kishner procedure.[10] A sixfold excess of hydrazine was required to give the best yield of fluorene.

References

1. A review of the Wolff-Kishner reduction is given by D. Todd, *in* "Organic Reactions" (R. Adams, ed.), Vol. IV, p. 378. Wiley, New York, 1948.
2. G. R. Clemo, R. Raper, and H. J. Vipond, *J. Chem. Soc.* p. 2095 (1949).
3. L. Wolff, *Ann. Chem. Liebigs* **394**, 86 (1912).
4. M. D. Soffer, M. B. Soffer, and K. W. Skerk, *J. Am. Chem. Soc.* **67**, 1435 (1945).
5. C. H. Herr, F. C. Whitmore, and R. W. Schiessler, *J. Am. Chem. Soc.* **67**, 2061 (1945).
6. Huang-Minlon, *J. Am. Chem. Soc.* **68**, 2487 (1946).
7. R. Hirschmann and W. S. Johnson, *J. Am. Chem. Soc.* **73**, 326 (1951).
8. D. H. R. Barton, D. A. J. Ives, and B. R. Thomas, *J. Chem. Soc.* p. 2056 (1955).
9. H. H. Szmant, H. F. Harnsberger, T. J. Butler, and W. P. Barie, *J. Am. Chem. Soc.* **74**, 2724–2728 (1952).
10. J. H. Weisburger and P. H. Grantham, *J. Org. Chem.* **21**, 1160 (1956).

Wurtz Reaction

Charles Adolphe Wurtz (1817–1884) was born in Strasbourg, France. After receiving the degree of Doctor of Medicine in 1843, Wurtz spent a year under Liebig at Giessen, where he became friends with A. W. Hofmann. In 1845, he was appointed assistant to Dumas (1800–1884) at the École de Médecine in Paris.

Eight years later, after Dumas' resignation, he was appointed to the Faculté de Médecine, and in 1874, a chair of organic chemistry was created for him at the Sorbonne. Among the students of Wurtz were Crafts, Fittig, Friedel, and van't Hoff. Wurtz with his teacher and friend, Dumas, contributed a great deal to the atomic theory and the concept of substitution in organic chemistry. It was in connection with the possibility of dimerization of radicals that Wurtz discovered the reaction which is associated with his name. Some of the other achievements of Wurtz include the discovery of methylamine (1849) and ethylene glycol (1856).

Wurtz, along with Dumas, Pasteur, and others, helped establish what is now the Société Chimique de France and its *Bulletin*.

* * *

Rudolf Fittig (1835–1910) was born in Hamburg, Germany. He studied under Wöhler at Göttingen and received the Ph.D. degree in 1858. After serving as an assistant to Wöhler, Fittig taught at Tübingen and then succeeded von Baeyer at Strassburg in 1876.

Fittig's contributions in chemistry were numerous. He discovered diphenyl, phenanthrene, coumarone, diacetyl, and the pinacone reaction. He synthesized mesitylene and α-naphthol, and showed that lactones were formed from γ-hydroxy acids.

The formation of paraffins by the reaction of an alkyl halide with metallic sodium is termed the Wurtz reaction.[1] The method is a general one and works best if a primary halide is employed.

$$2RX + 2Na \longrightarrow R{\cdot}R + 2NaX$$

255

For example, two moles of n-butyl iodide react to give n-octane. With a tertiary halide the product is an olefin. If two different alkyl radicals are involved in the reaction, a mixture of products is obtained which may be difficult to separate. In this connection, it has been shown[2] that with n-butyl bromide and n-hexyl bromide the ratio of products is n-octane, 27.5%; n-decane, 43.5%; and n-dodecane, 29.0%.

The mechanism of the Wurtz reaction has been interpreted in terms of both free radicals and organometallic compounds.[3,4] Simple alkyl halides have been shown[5] to react with sodium under mild conditions to form the organosodium derivative which then can react with more alkyl halide to give a hydrocarbon.

$$RX + 2Na \longrightarrow RNa + NaX$$

$$RNa + RX \longrightarrow R{\cdot}R + NaX$$

At low temperatures the reaction of the alkyl halide with sodium can be interrupted at the organometallic stage, and the presence of this intermediate has been demonstrated by carbonation to the corresponding acid.

$$RNa \xrightarrow{CO_2} RCOOH$$

Letsinger[6] has reported that when benzyl sodium reacts with optically-active 2-bromobutane, an optically-active 2-benzylbutane is obtained.

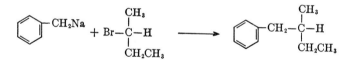

It has also been shown that in the Wurtz reaction involving (—)-2-chlorooctane with sodium there is an inversion of configuration of the carbon atom bearing the chlorine.[7] The product is (—)-7,8-dimethyltetradecane.

$$Cl-\underset{\underset{C_6H_{13}}{|}}{\overset{\overset{CH_3}{|}}{C}}-H \xrightarrow{Na} H-\underset{\underset{C_6H_{13}}{|}}{\overset{\overset{CH_3}{|}}{C}}-\underset{\underset{CH_3}{|}}{\overset{\overset{C_6H_{13}}{|}}{C}}-H$$

This has been offered as evidence for a nucleophilic displacement reaction involving an intermediate sodium alkyl. Whether inversion or

256

racemization occurs during the Wurtz reaction appears to depend upon the nature of the organosodium compound and the alkyl halide.

Fittig reaction. A process which is similar to the Wurtz reaction but which involves the reaction of aryl halides with metallic sodium is called the Fittig reaction. The yields of the expected diaryl compounds are usually very low.

Wurtz-Fittig reaction. When a mixture of an alkyl and aryl halide is used, the reaction is called the Wurtz-Fittig reaction. This process offers a very satisfactory method for the preparation of aralkyl hydrocarbons. The synthesis of *n*-butylbenzene from *n*-butyl bromide and bromobenzene is an example of the Wurtz-Fittig reaction.[8]

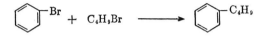

References

1. A. Wurtz, *Ann. Chem. Liebigs* **96**, 364 (1855).
2. H. W. Davis, W. R. Gilkerson, and H. H. Hernandez, *J. Chem. Educ.* **26**, 606 (1949).
3. See E. R. Alexander, "Principles of Ionic Organic Reactions," pp. 203–206. Wiley, New York, 1950.
4. A discussion of the Wurtz reaction in terms of a free radical mechanism is given by M. Tuot, *Bull. soc. chim. France* p. 291 (1948).
5. A. A. Morton and I. Hechenbleikner, *J. Am. Chem. Soc.* **58**, 1697 (1936).
6. R. L. Letsinger, *J. Am. Chem. Soc.* **70**, 406 (1948).
7. E. LeGoff, S. E. Ulrich, and D. B. Denney, *J. Am. Chem. Soc.* **80**, 622 (1958).
8. R. R. Read, L. S. Foster, A. Russel, and V. L. Simril, *in* "Organic Syntheses" (W. E. Bachmann, ed.), Vol. 25, p. 11. Wiley, New York, 1945.

Subject Index

A

Acetaldehyde, 4-methoxyphenyl-, preparation, 223

Acetamide, phenyl-, preparation, 241

Acetic acid, α-bromophenyl-, ethyl ester, preparation, 131

chloro, ethyl ester, condensation, with ethyl β-benzoylpropionate, 69

cyclopropyl ester, preparation, 6

3, 4-dimethoxyphenyl-, preparation, 93

naphthyl-, in Pschorr synthesis, 199

phenyl, halomagnesium derivative (Ivanov reagent), 143

halomagnesium derivative, reaction, with carbonyl compounds (Ivanov reaction), 143

tertiary amides of, in Ivanov reaction, 144

trifluoroperoxy, in Baeyer-Villiger reaction, 5

Acetic acids, aryl, reaction, with o-nitrobenzaldehyde, 198

Acetic anhydride, in Perkin reaction, 184

Acetoacetic acid, ethyl ester, see Ethyl acetoacetate

Acetoacetonitrile, α-phenyl, preparation, 47

Acetone, condensation, with diethyl succinate, 228

in Claisen condensation, 47

preparation, from 2-nitropropane, 175

Acetonedicarboxylic acid, diethyl ester, in Knorr pyrrole synthesis, 151

Acetonitrile, condensation, with resorcinol, 132

3,4-dihydroxyphenyl-, preparation, 65

4-methoxyphenyl-, in Stephen reaction, 223

phenyl-, 47, 143

trichloro-, in Hoesch synthesis, 133

trifluoro-, in Hoesch synthesis, 133

Acetonitriles, aryl, preparation, from α-keto acids, 94

Acetophenone, 2-acylamino-, formation of hydroxyquinolines from, 39

3,5-bis(chloromethyl)-2-hydroxy-, preparation, 25

5-chloromethyl-2-hydroxy-, preparation, 25

condensation, with ethyl α-bromopropionate, 200

5-cyanomethyl-2-hydroxy-, oxidation, with hydrogen peroxide, 65

2,4-dihydroxy-, preparation, 132

2,4-dihydroxy-6-methoxy-ω-trichloro-preparation, 133

2,4-dihydroxy-ω-trifluoro, preparation, 133

2-hydroxy-, chloromethylation, 25

2-hydroxy-3,4-dimethyl-, in Dakin oxidation, 65

preparation, by acylation of benzene, 102

reduction, 55

tetrahydro-, preparation, 70, 71

in Willgerodt reaction, 241

Aceturic acid, see Acetyl glycine

Acetyl chloride, in Darzens ketone synthesis, 70

in Friedel-Crafts reaction, 102

reaction, with cycloheptene, 70

Acetylacetone, condensation, with aniline, 57

Acetylenedicarboxylic acid, reaction, with butadiene, 79

Acetylenes, conversion to amides, 241

D

T

U